The **Experiential** Gospel of

John

A GUIDED DISCIPLESHIP JOURNEY IN A SPIRIT-EMPOWERED FAITH

A global network empowering people to experience and reproduce great relationships through loving God and others

For more information contact:

The Great Commandment Network
2511 South Lakeline Blvd., Cedar Park, TX 78613
www.greatcommandment.net
800.881.8008

Table of Contents

Introduction vii
Preface to the Passion Translation viii
How To Use This Resource ix

John 1. 1
Engage Fellowship 3
Encounter Jesus 4
Experience Scripture 5
My Journal. 6

John 2. 7
Experience Scripture 9
Encounter Jesus 10
Engage Fellowship 11
My Journal. 12

John 3. 13
Engage Fellowship 15
Encounter Jesus 16
Experience Scripture 17
My Journal. 18

John 4. 19
Encounter Jesus 21
Experience Scripture 22
Engage Fellowship 23
My Journal. 24

John 5. 25
Encounter Jesus 27
Engage Fellowship 28
Experience Scripture 29
My Journal. 30

John 6. 31
Encounter Jesus 33
Experience Scripture 34
Engage Fellowship 35
My Journal. 36

John 7 37
Experience Scripture 39
Encounter Jesus 40
Engage Fellowship 41
My Journal 42

John 8 43
Engage Fellowship 45
Encounter Jesus 46
Experience Scripture 47
My Journal 48

John 9 49
Encounter Jesus 51
Engage Fellowship 52
Experience Scripture 53
My Journal 54

John 10 55
Engage Fellowship 57
Encounter Jesus 58
Experience Scripture 59
My Journal 60

John 11 61
Engage Fellowship 63
Experience Scripture 64
Encounter Jesus 65
My Journal 66

John 12 67
Engage Fellowship 69
Encounter Jesus 70
Experience Scripture 71
My Journal 72

John 13 73
Experience Scripture 75
Encounter Jesus 76
Engage Fellowship 77
My Journal 78

John 14 79
Encounter Jesus 81
Experience Scripture 82
Encounter Jesus 83
My Journal 84

John 15. 85

Encounter Jesus 87

Engage Fellowship 88

Experience Scripture 89

My Journal. 90

John 16. 91

Experience Scripture 93

Engage Fellowship 94

Encounter Jesus 95

My Journal. 96

John 17. 97

Encounter Jesus 99

Experience Scripture 100

Engage Fellowship 101

My Journal. 102

John 18. 103

Experience Scripture 105

Engage Fellowship 106

Encounter Jesus 107

My Journal. 108

John 19. 109

Encounter Jesus 111

Experience Scripture 112

Experience Scripture 113

My Journal. 114

John 20. 115

Experience Scripture 117

Engage Fellowship 118

Encounter Jesus 119

My Journal. 120

John 21. 121

Encounter Jesus 123

Experience Scripture 124

Engage Fellowship 125

My Journal. 126

About the Great Commandment Network. 129

Introduction to Outcomes 130

Spirit-Empowered Faith Outcomes. 132

Age-Stage Model. 136

Resources. 138

Introduction

THE EXPERIENTIAL GOSPEL OF JOHN is designed to engage followers of Jesus as they impart both the gospel and live out a relevant, daily faith (1 Thessalonians 2:7–8). This resource is unique because the exercises in each chapter were written with the specific goal of engaging you in a Spirit-empowered faith. These exercises are created to move beyond seeking to simply know or study God's truth and move toward actually experiencing it. Why is this important? It's only an experiential, Spirit-empowered faith that can change our lives and the lives of those around us.

Imagine this: You've just begun a journey in the *Experiential Gospel of John*. It's as if you're going for a walk. As you read and work through this resource, we invite you to walk:

- In the Light of God's Son—John 8:12
- In the Light of God's Word—Psalm 119:105
- In the Light of God's People—Matthew 5:14

The exercises in this resource are designed around these three sources of God's light. They'll encourage your journey as a Spirit-empowered disciple of Jesus.

We've also included a framework for your growth journey. The framework provides 40 outcomes that serve as markers of your spiritual growth. The 40 outcomes are organized around the Spirit-empowered discipleship framework:

- Love the Lord (Outcomes L1–L10)
- Live His Word (Outcomes W1–W10)
- Love People (Outcomes P1–P10)
- Live His Mission (Outcomes M1–M10)

We're delighted that you've decided to take this walk with us. God's Word reminds us that it's vitally important to walk in the light. *"... Walk in the light lest the darkness overtake you"* (John 12:35). May your journey with Jesus, His Word, and His people produce life change like you've never seen before.

The Great Commandment Network is committed to empowering people in how to experience and reproduce great relationships—with God and one another. Toward that goal, we have developed the experiential exercises and collaborated with a broad spectrum of global leaders to develop the Spirit-empowered discipleship framework, and the Spirit-empowered outcomes included in the appendix of this resource (see pages 129–132). Special thanks to Pastor Dennis Gallaher, Dr. Lewis Alexander, and Dr. David Ferguson for their gifted writing, their contributions, and perspectives.

Terri Snead
Executive Editor, Great Commandment Network

Preface to the Passion Translation

by Dr. Brian Simmons

"FOR THIS IS HOW MUCH GOD LOVED THE WORLD—HE GAVE HIS ONE AND ONLY UNIQUE SON AS A GIFT. SO NOW EVERYONE WHO BELIEVES IN HIM WILL NEVER PERISH BUT EXPERIENCE EVERLASTING LIFE."

—JOHN 3:16

THE PASSION TRANSLATION is a new, heart-level translation that expresses God's fiery heart of love to this generation using Hebrew, Greek, and Aramaic manuscripts, merging the emotion and life-changing truth of God's Word.

So why another translation? Many wonderful versions of our Bible now grace our bookshelves, bookstores, software programs, even apps on our phones. So why add one more? The reason is simple: God longs to have his Word expressed in every language in a way that unlocks the passion of his heart. The goal of this work is to trigger inside every reader an overwhelming response to the truth of the Bible, revealing the deep mysteries of the Scriptures in the love language of God, the language of the heart.

If you're hungry for God and want to know Him on a deeper level, The Passion Translation will help you encounter God's heart and discover what He has for your life.

Dr. Brian Simmons
Lead Translator for The Passion Translation

Brian Simmons is the author of numerous books that promote the redemption and reconciliation of the nations through Christ and extension of His kingdom. Currently he is working on a new, fresh, dynamic-equivalent translation of the entire Bible, called The Passion Translation.

How to Use This Resource

This resource has been specifically designed for a variety of uses including personal devotions, small groups, Bible study classes, and one-on-one or group discipleship. It is often used to accompany the sermon and teaching series.

Four distinct elements are included for each chapter as a framework for spiritual formation:

1. **A DAILY Guided Reading Plan**—Imperative to living a Spirit-empowered faith is to embrace the WORD as "living and active" as the Holy Spirit leads the reader into a deeper love relationship with the God of the Word and with those He loves (Matthew 22:40). **This two-page element seeks to guide *daily reading of the whole chapter* with a focus on discipleship outcomes—one for each day.**

   - DAY 1 Spirit-empowered Faith Outcome L-3:
   Experiencing God *as He really is through deepened intimacy with Him*

   - DAY 2 Spirit-empowered Faith Outcome W-1:
   Focusing on frequently being led by the Spirit into deeper love for the One who wrote the Word

   - DAY 3 Spirit-empowered Faith Outcome P-5:
   Focusing on ministering His life and love to our nearest ones at home and with family as well as faithful engagement in His Body, the church

   - DAY 4 Spirit-empowered Faith Outcome M-1:
   Focusing on imparting the gospel and one's very life in daily activities and relationships, vocation, and community

   - DAY 5 Spirit-empowered Faith Outcome L-4:
   Focusing on rejoicing regularly in my identity as "His Beloved"

2. WEEKLY **Encounter with Jesus**—As the Holy Spirit leads the reader of the Word into a fresh encounter with Jesus, transformation happens. This one-page element for each chapter of John focuses the readers meditation and mindful reflection on Jesus, the One who is still transforming lives today! Reflect on this reality all across the Gospels...Zaccheus, Bartemaus, the woman at the well, the woman caught in adultery, Nicodemus, and countless others encountered Jesus and went away forever changed! It still happens today as His Spirit leads the reader of the Word to encounter this One who is "the same yesterday, today, and forever" (Hebrews 13:8).

3. WEEKLY **"Practice" of Experiencing Scripture**—The study of the Word is critical, and memorizing verses is encouraged, but it's actually "doing God's Word" that transforms us and others. Research in discipleship such

as the *Willowcreek REVEAL Study* concludes that it's this "weekly" living of our faith that truly produces fully devoted followers. Consider that as the Holy Spirit leads you to encounter God at the point of His Word, something CHANGES, and it's NOT God, and it's NOT His Word—it's YOU!

- This Experiencing Scripture element for each chapter of John provides a Bible verse to be lived and practiced this WEEK. It's this lifestyle of "doing the book" that moves my faith journey from exploring and embracing truth to experiencing it in all my relationships such that it becomes expressed as "who I am," my identity! (See the Age-Stage Model pp. 136–137)

- Sometimes the verse for the WEEK is experienced or practiced (vertically) with the Lord as called for in Psalm 100:2, "Serve the Lord with gladness."

- Sometimes the verse for the WEEK is experienced (horizontally) with others as called for in Romans 12:15, "Rejoice with those who rejoice and mourn with those who mourn."

Jesus champions this "relational" approach to Scripture (hermeneutic) in Matthew 22:40 and Mark 12:31. He urges that Scripture depends or "hangs upon" loving God (vertically) and loving others (horizontally). Paul would reaffirm this importance of love as he references "knowledge (even of the Word) can make us arrogant, but it's LOVE that builds us up into the likeness of Jesus" (1 Corinthians 8:1).

4. **WEEKLY Engagement in Fellowship**—Whether in one-on-one discipleship, bible studies, or small groups, this one-page element for each chapter of John's gospel gives focus to "imparting our very lives" to one another as we gather for this week's meeting (1 Peter 1:7–8).

    A weekly meeting might then include:

    - A recap of personal insights and deepened intimacy with the Lord through the DAILY Guided Reading Plan

    - Celebrating together this WEEK'S Encounter with Jesus as each follower reflects on the Spirit's fresh work of Christ-likeness

    - Sharing a story of this WEEK'S Experiencing Scripture as it was practiced with the Lord, with our families and friends, in our vocation, and with others who need to know Jesus

    - Significant time focused on living out the Engaging Fellowship exercise

Since some of God's light and love is in His people, it will be important for mentors and small groups to spend time completing the Engaging Fellowship sections of the text as they seek to fervently love one another form the heart (1 Peter 1:22). Becoming more like Jesus is realized when we take the time to truly fellowship with other Jesus followers.

"'Love the Lord your God

with every passion of your heart,

with all the energy of your being,

and with every thought that is within you.'

This is the great and supreme commandment.

And the second is like it in importance:

'You must love your friend

in the same way you love yourself.'

Contained within these commandments to love

you will find all the meaning of the Law

and the Prophets."

—Matthew 22: 37–40 (TPT)

John 1

…love your neighbor as yourself. On these two commandments depend the whole Law and the Prophets" (see Matthew 22:37–40 NASB).

REREAD JOHN 1 EACH DAY REFLECTING ON A DIFFERENT ASPECT OF HIS LOVE.

DAY 1

L3

Experiencing God as He really is through deepened intimacy with Him

I. **Reflect on how the REAL God is a God of love.** How might this text lead me to better love God? "We love because He first loved us" (1 John 4:19 NASB). We can only love the REAL God with all our "heart, soul, mind, and strength."

A. As you read and reflect on the chapter, how might you describe the REAL God as He is seen as Father, Son, and Holy Spirit?

1. In verse_____, He is seen as _____
_____ .

2. In verse _____, He is seen as _____
_____ .

3. In verse _____ , the love of Jesus is seen toward_____
as He _____ .

4. In verse _____ , the love of Jesus is seen toward_____
as He _____ .

5. How might these insights challenge some of your misconceptions of God?

Sadly, I sometimes mistakenly see God as _____
_____ .

DAY 2

W1

Frequently being led by the Spirit into deeper love for the One who wrote the Word

B. **Reflect on how God has loved *you*** since He is the same yesterday, today, and forever (Hebrews 13:8). **Pause to let Him love you.**

1. *Father, as you express yourself to me as the God who* _____
_____ , *my heart is moved with*
_____ .

2. *Father, as you express yourself to me as the God who* _____
_____ , *my heart is moved with*
_____ .

C. Jesus is available to love you like we read of His love in this chapter. Pause to express your heart to Him as you see Him in this chapter.

1. Describe how Jesus has loved you in some of the same ways that you read of His love in this chapter:

I have experienced the love of Jesus as He has _____
_____ .

2. *Jesus, as you love me like you loved those in this chapter, my heart is touched with* _____ .

DAY 3

P5

Ministering His life and love to our nearest ones at home and with family as well as faithful engagement in His body, the church

II. **Reflect on how you can better love your "near ones."** How might this text lead me to better love others? "As I have loved you, so you also should love one another" (John 13:34 NASB).

Since we have freely received of His love, we are to freely give this same love to others. Consider again how you see love portrayed in this chapter.

A. Who among your family or friends might you better love?

1. *I could better love_____,*
   especially by _____.

DAY 4

M1

Imparting the gospel and one's very life in daily activities and relationships, vocation and community

B. **Reflect on how you might be a witness of His love.** Notice again how Jesus expressed love by accepting, forgiving, or sacrificing? How might Jesus have taken initiative, expressed compassion, offered support, shared truth, and eternal hope?

1. Who in the traffic patterns of your life might benefit from receiving the blessing of Christ's love through you?
   (Who)_____could benefit from my sharing the love of Jesus by _____.

2. Who in your life could benefit from sharing part of your life story of encountering truth and eternal hope?
   (Who)_____could benefit from my sharing more of
   _____.

3. Pause now to pray for this person and then for yourself as you impart both your life and the gospel.

DAY 5

L4

Rejoicing regularly in my identity as "His Beloved"

III. **Reflect on *you* as the recipient of His love.** Your significance, value, and worth have been established by your Creator through the gift of His Son. How might this text affirm your identity as "His Beloved"?

"The light of God's love shined within us when he sent his matchless Son into the world so that we might live through him" (1 John 4:9).

Celebrate how you have received His love and grace, His forgiveness and new life, His calling and kingdom purpose.

A. Reread the text as His truth being shared just for you.

1. *I'm grateful that I have experienced the blessing of verse _____*
   as I _____.

B. Since He is the same yesterday, today, and forever, meditate on your being *in* the story of this chapter. Allow Him to love you as you read of His love in the chapter.

1. *My heart is touched with gratitude that Jesus _____*
   _____.

Walking in the Light of God's People

Through Faithful Engagement in Fellowship   John 12:35; Matthew 5:14

"And this 'Living Expression' is the Light that bursts through gloom—the Light that darkness could not diminish!" (John 1:5).

Notice that the Light shines in the present tense—not just in the past but now! Certainly it was Christ the Word who became flesh and dwelt among men as Light, but He still today shines as Light in the darkness. We have both a *historical* Jesus who was with God and became man, but this same Jesus is *contemporary* as Light shining in darkness.

How confusing it must have been for the disciples to grasp the significance of Christ's words, "You are the light of the world" (Matthew 5:14 NASB). But as the resurrection and ascension unfolded, the coming of the Holy Spirit ushered in the fulfillment of Christ's words. No doubt, God's light is made known through the Son and the Word, but there's more (John 8:12; Psalm 119:105). His light is to be made manifest through His people! As followers of Jesus, you and I have been have been made partakers of divine light, and this light exposes darkness. Sometimes the darkness exposed is in the culture or in those who walk in darkness, and sometimes the darkness is in me!

Sometimes it's the quiet conviction of His Spirit that exposes in me the darkness of sin and the flesh. At at other times, it is the light of Christ in fellow saints that reveals in me the darkness of inconsistencies in my walk with Jesus.

Yielding to the Spirit's fullness as life in the Spirit brings supernatural intimacy with the Lord, manifestation of divine gifts and witness of the fruit of the Spirit

- Prevailing patience in a friend reveals my irritable impatience.

- Courageous witness in a fellow disciple exposes the timidity of my faith.

- A family member's compassionate engagement with those in need stands in sharp contrast to my cold indifference.

His light made known through others has revealed in me measures of darkness that need the transforming work of His Spirit. As a follower who has been exhorted by Jesus to "walk in the light" (John 12:35), it seems important to embrace the light of true fellowship. Rather than avoid the illuminating power of light, let's welcome it!

Pause to pray with a partner or small group.

Ask the Holy Spirit to show you Jesus in the lives of fellow disciples that you might find freedom from sin and self to grow in your Christ-likeness.

Holy Spirit, challenge me through the light of Jesus in other disciples that you might perfect in me more and more of His likeness. I'm especially touched by how you make Jesus known through _____
as he/she expresses _____
_____.

Walking in the Light of God's Son

Through Fresh Encounters With Jesus   John 12:35; John 8:12

"...He will be the One I have sent to baptize with the Holy Spirit" (John 1:33).

John's wilderness cry was to a baptism of repentance, but One greater than he would send forth a different baptism. Ushered in at Pentecost, the promise of the Holy Spirit is now available. Followers of Jesus yielding to this baptism will experience rivers of living water as the fruit of the Holy Spirit is made known (John 7:28; Galatians 5:22).

Reflect quietly on the many facets of the Holy Spirit's fruit: "but the fruit of the Spirit is . . ."

Pause to yield in a fresh way to the fullness of His Spirit. Listen as the Spirit whispers about a needed, deepened work that you might more clearly manifest His fruit. Might you need a fresh work of:

L9

Yielding to the Spirit's fullness as life in the Spirit brings supernatural intimacy with the Lord, manifestation of divine gifts and witness of the fruit of the Spirit

- His love, joy, or peace?

- His patience, kindness, or goodness?

- His faithfulness, gentleness, or self-control?

Listen to His invitation and yield to its promise: "Come unto me and out of your innermost being will flow rivers of living water."

Ask for the Spirit to empower this deepened work in and through you. Claim the promise of 1 John 5:14–15, "If you ask anything according to His will (confident that you're expressing the Spirit's fruit is His will)...He will HEAR...and you will HAVE!"

Lord Jesus I need a deepened work of _____
(love, joy, peace, patience, etc.) in order that I might more clearly reveal the Spirit's fruit in my life. Fill and empower me, Holy Spirit, as I give witness of you.

Walking in the Light of God's Word

Through Frequent Experience of Scripture   John 12:35; Psalm 119:105

"Jesus said . . . 'follow Me'" (John 1:43).

Two simple but profound words can guide my daily walk as light in a dark world: "Follow me." Whatever may come my way today, Jesus has gone before me; He has led, and I'm to follow! "WWJD" is my key to following.

- What would Jesus DO becomes a guiding principle when uncertainty abounds.

- What would Jesus CHOOSE guides me away from a broad road of destruction onto the narrow road of life abundant.

- What would Jesus SAY guides the words of my mouth away from unwholesome words and into words that edify.

- What would Jesus THINK guides my thoughts away from this world into His Word, which renews my mind.

- Clarity and adequacy for daily living is found in the powerful simplicity of two words from the Word: "Follow Me."

Pause to celebrate with a partner or small group:

Recently, I sensed an important 'following' of Jesus as I faced _____ _____

and found strength to _____.

L9

Yielding to the Spirit's fullness as life in the Spirit brings supernatural intimacy with the Lord, manifestation of divine gifts and witness of the fruit of the Spirit

OUR PRAYER as you read, reflect, and embrace John's words is simple. With Paul the apostle, we pray, "that the eyes of your heart be enlightened, so that you will know what is the hope of His calling, what are the riches of the glory of His inheritance in the saints, and what is the surpassing greatness of His power towards us who believe" (Ephesians 1:18–19 NASB). May the rich treasure of the Father's passionate love capture and overflow your life with His greater grace!

Yielding to the Spirit's fullness as life in the Spirit brings supernatural intimacy with the Lord, manifestation of divine gifts and witness of the fruit of the Spirit

John 2

REREAD JOHN 2 EACH DAY REFLECTING ON A DIFFERENT ASPECT OF HIS LOVE.

DAY 1

Experiencing God as He really is through deepened intimacy with Him

I. **Reflect on how the REAL God is a God of love.** How might this text lead me to better love God? "We love because He first loved us" (1 John 4:19 NASB). We can only love the REAL God with all our "heart, soul, mind, and strength."

A. As you read and reflect on the chapter, how might you describe the REAL God as He is seen as Father, Son, and Holy Spirit?

1. In verse_____, He is seen as _____
   _____ .

2. In verse _____, He is seen as _____
   _____ .

3. In verse _____ , the love of Jesus is seen toward_____
   as He _____ .

4. In verse _____ , the love of Jesus is seen toward_____
   as He _____ .

5. How might these insights challenge some of your misconceptions of God?

   Sadly, I sometimes mistakenly see God as _____
   _____ .

DAY 2

Frequently being led by the Spirit into deeper love for the One who wrote the Word

B. **Reflect on how God has loved *you*** since He is the same yesterday, today, and forever (Hebrews 13:8). **Pause to let Him love you.**

1. *Father, as you express yourself to me as the God who* _____
   _____, *my heart is moved with*
   _____ .

2. *Father, as you express yourself to me as the God who* _____
   _____, *my heart is moved with*
   _____ .

C. Jesus is available to love you like we read of His love in this chapter. Pause to express your heart to Him as you see Him in this chapter.

1. Describe how Jesus has loved you in some of the same ways that you read of His love in this chapter:

   I have experienced the love of Jesus as He has _____
   _____ .

2. *Jesus, as you love me like you loved those in this chapter, my heart is touched with* _____ .

DAY 3

P5

Ministering His life and love to our nearest ones at home and with family as well as faithful engagement in His body, the church

II. **Reflect on how you can better love your "near ones."** How might this text lead me to better love others? "As I have loved you, so you also should love one another." (John 13:34 NASB).

Since we have freely received of His love, we are to freely give this same love to others. Consider again how you see love portrayed in this chapter.

A. Who among your family or friends might you better love?

1. *I could better love_____,*
   especially by _____.

DAY 4

M1

Imparting the gospel and one's very life in daily activities and relationships, vocation and community

B. **Reflect on how you might be a witness of His love.** Notice again how Jesus expressed love by accepting, forgiving, or sacrificing? How might Jesus have taken initiative, expressed compassion, offered support, shared truth, and eternal hope?

1. Who in the traffic patterns of your life might benefit from receiving the blessing of Christ's love through you?
   (Who)_____could benefit from my sharing the love of Jesus by _____.

2. Who in your life could benefit from sharing part of your life story of encountering truth and eternal hope?
   (Who)_____could benefit from my sharing more of
   _____.

3. Pause now to pray for this person and then for yourself as you impart both your life and the gospel.

DAY 5

L4

Rejoicing regularly in my identity as "His Beloved"

III. **Reflect on *you* as the recipient of His love.** Your significance, value, and worth have been established by your Creator through the gift of His Son. How might this text affirm your identity as "His Beloved"?

"The light of God's love shined within us when he sent his matchless Son into the world so that we might live through him." (1 John 4:9).

Celebrate how you have received His love and grace, His forgiveness and new life, His calling and kingdom purpose.

A. Reread the text as His truth being shared just for you.

1. *I'm grateful that I have experienced the blessing of verse _____*
   as I _____.

B. Since He is the same yesterday, today, and forever, meditate on your being *in* the story of this chapter. Allow Him to love you as you read of His love in the chapter.

1. *My heart is touched with gratitude that Jesus _____*
   _____.

Walking in the Light of God's Word

Through Frequent Experience of Scripture   John 12:35; Psalm 119:105

"Whatever Jesus tells you, make sure that you do it!" (John 2:5).

What an awesome key to life abundant and a life pleasing to the Lord! This was the simple secret of Jesus' love for the Father. Nowhere in Scripture does it speak of the Father obeying the Son, but uniquely, the Son loves the Father by "doing whatever the Father asks."

Jesus would describe His own love of His Father with these words: "I am doing exactly what the Father destined for me to accomplish, so that the world will discover how much I love my Father" (John 14:31).

The Son loves the Father by *yielding* to the Father's every word, and so it's to be with His followers. Sometimes His speaking is through His Word or a fellow disciple; sometimes He speaks in prayer, and at other times, it's the gentle impression of the Holy Spirit upon our spirit. Implicit to this life in the Spirit is:

- First saying "yes" by faith even before we've heard Him speak.
- Next "hearing" the Lord as we faithfully yield to young Samuel's prayer; "speak Lord for your servant is listening" (1 Samuel 3:8–9 NASB).
- Finally full and immediate obedience to what we hear.

The first miracle at the wedding feast of Cana illustrates the powerful simplicity of "doing what He says." Our daily accountability to do the same will empower a fulfilling and impactful life.

Consider this discipline as you reflect on the close of each day:

"Lord, today I heard you say _____
and your Spirit empowered me to _____
_____
_____
_____.

M2

Expressing and extending the Kingdom of God as compassion, justice, love, and forgiveness are shared

Walking in the Light of God's Son

Through Fresh Encounters With Jesus   John 12:35; John 8:12

"I am consumed with a fiery passion to keep your house pure!" (John 2:17).

What are you truly zealous about? What stirs your waking moments and keeps you awake often or fuels your passion? Is it of this world or His? As you consider a response, review your thought life and time commitments, your generosity and compassionate involvement with others.

Being zealous for the things of God and His kingdom gives meaning and legacy to the Christ-follower's life. Christ's response in the temple was not "politically correct" or without personal risk. Righteous anger prompted Him to action. His Father's plans and purposes were given priority above mere man's.

Pause quietly, asking His Spirit to reveal and refine the passions of your heart:

■ In what ways has His Spirit recently led you counter to "political correctness" as a witness of Him?

■ What risks of being misunderstood or rejected has He recently led you to take?

■ What kingdom actions has His righteous anger led you to take?

■ What eternal plans and purposes are parts of your daily priorities?

Now pray for a fresh encounter with Jesus and His zeal:

"Lord Jesus, make the words of my mouth, the meditations of my heart, and my actions each day pleasing in Thy sight. Holy Spirit, fill me with fresh zeal for eternal things that others around me might take note that I have been with Jesus."

SPIRIT EMPOWERED *Faith*

M2

Expressing and extending the Kingdom of God as compassion, justice, love, and forgiveness are shared

Walking in the Light of God's People

Through Faithful Engagement in Fellowship   John 12:35; Matthew 5:14

"[T]he disciples . . . believed the Scripture and what Jesus had said" (John 2:22).

M2

Expressing and extending the Kingdom of God as compassion, justice, love, and forgiveness are shared

God has NOT left us without instruction, but rather through His Word, He has given us truth, and His truth sets us free (John 8:32). In these very early days of the ministry of Jesus, we see the imperative of living daily in believing faith and action based upon His Word. It was the words of Jesus that:

- Provided secure direction.

- Separated faith from unbelief.

- Served as ultimate authority for life and eternity.

- Brought unity out of division as His followers yielded to the Word.

Such are some of the many blessings from being a follower, who like these early disciples, "believed the word."

Pause to reflect and share your own testimonies of believing the Word:

Recently the Word provided me direction regarding _____
_____.

A scriptural promise that I'm now believing in faith will become real would be
_____
_____
_____.

Even though everything around me says differently, I hold to the authority of the Scripture that _____
_____
_____.

I've recently seen His Word bring unity out of division in my own life as I experienced the truth of _____
_____
_____.

Share together with your small group or partner at least one of the above ways in which, as His disciple, you are "believing His Word."

Then pray together that each day might be characterized by "walking in the light of His Word" (John 12:35; Psalm 119:105).

Dear Holy Spirit, as the One who authored the Word, please lead me often into embracing by faith it's life-giving power; might I reflect often that this day I brought you pleasure by being a "doer" of the Word (James 1:22).

My Journal

M2

Expressing and extending the Kingdom of God as compassion, justice, love, and forgiveness are shared

John 3

…and love your neighbor as you love yourself. The whole law and the prophets depend on these two commandments" (Matthew 22:37–40 NASB).

REREAD JOHN 3 EACH DAY REFLECTING ON A DIFFERENT ASPECT OF HIS LOVE.

DAY 1

L3

Experiencing God as He really is through deepened intimacy with Him

I. **Reflect on how the REAL God is a God of love.** How might this text lead me to better love God? "We love because He first loved us" (1 John 4:19 NASB). We can only love the REAL God with all our "heart, soul, mind, and strength."

A. As you read and reflect on the chapter, how might you describe the REAL God as He is seen as Father, Son, and Holy Spirit?

1. In verse_____, He is seen as _____
_____.

2. In verse _____, He is seen as _____
_____.

3. In verse _____, the love of Jesus is seen toward_____
as He _____.

4. In verse _____, the love of Jesus is seen toward_____
as He _____.

5. How might these insights challenge some of your misconceptions of God?

Sadly, I sometimes mistakenly see God as _____
_____.

DAY 2

W1

Frequently being led by the Spirit into deeper love for the One who wrote the Word

B. **Reflect on how God has loved *you*** since He is the same yesterday, today, and forever (Hebrews 13:8). **Pause to let Him love you.**

1. *Father, as you express yourself to me as the God who* _____
_____, *my heart is moved with*
_____.

2. *Father, as you express yourself to me as the God who* _____
_____, *my heart is moved with*
_____.

C. Jesus is available to love you like we read of His love in this chapter. Pause to express your heart to Him as you see Him in this chapter.

1. Describe how Jesus has loved you in some of the same ways that you read of His love in this chapter:

I have experienced the love of Jesus as He has _____
_____.

2. *Jesus, as you love me like you loved those in this chapter, my heart is touched with* _____.

DAY 3

P5

Ministering His life and love to our nearest ones at home and with family as well as faithful engagement in His body, the church

II. **Reflect on how you can better love your "near ones."** How might this text lead me to better love others? "As I have loved you, so you also should love one another." (John 13:34 NASB).

Since we have freely received of His love, we are to freely give this same love to others. Consider again how you see love portrayed in this chapter.

A. Who among your family or friends might you better love?

1. *I could better love_____,
especially by _____.*

DAY 4

M1

Imparting the gospel and one's very life in daily activities and relationships, vocation and community

B. **Reflect on how you might be a witness of His love.** Notice again how Jesus expressed love by accepting, forgiving, or sacrificing? How might Jesus have taken initiative, expressed compassion, offered support, shared truth, and eternal hope?

1. Who in the traffic patterns of your life might benefit from receiving the blessing of Christ's love through you?
(Who)_____could benefit from my sharing the love of Jesus by _____.

2. Who in your life could benefit from sharing part of your life story of encountering truth and eternal hope?
(Who)_____could benefit from my sharing more of _____.

3. Pause now to pray for this person and then for yourself as you impart both your life and the gospel.

DAY 5

L4

Rejoicing regularly in my identity as "His Beloved"

III. **Reflect on *you* as the recipient of His love.** Your significance, value, and worth have been established by your Creator through the gift of His Son. How might this text affirm your identity as "His Beloved"?

"The light of God's love shined within us when he sent his matchless Son into the world so that we might live through him." (1 John 4:9).

Celebrate how you have received His love and grace, His forgiveness and new life, His calling and kingdom purpose.

A. Reread the text as His truth being shared just for you.

1. *I'm grateful that I have experienced the blessing of verse _____
as I _____.*

B. Since He is the same yesterday, today, and forever, meditate on your being *in* the story of this chapter. Allow Him to love you as you read of His love in the chapter.

1. *My heart is touched with gratitude that Jesus _____
_____.*

Walking in the Light of God's People

Through Faithful Engagement in Fellowship   John 12:35; Matthew 5:14

"You shouldn't be amazed by my statement 'You must be born from above!'" (John 3:7).

W6

Encountering Jesus in the Word for deepened transformation in Christ-likeness

This discourse between Jesus and Nicodemus has personal relevance to each person "born of woman," to each of us, to you, to me. It's this shared experience of being born again that makes us part of His family, a shared community of Jesus followers.

In His family, we, like Nicodemus, have been challenged to embrace Him as more than "teacher" but also to receive Him as Lord. We, like Nicodemus, have been provided the opportunity to add to our natural life, His supernatural life.

It's this miracle of being "Spirit-born" that unites us by the Holy Spirit to both Jesus and to one another. It's this connection of the born-again that creates true fellowship, a community of Spirit-empowered followers who embrace the imperative to "let us run with endurance the race set before us, fixing our eyes on Jesus, the author and perfecter of our faith" (Hebrews 12:1–2 NASB). The pursuit of revival and spiritual awakening is for "US," not a solo race but for a community of Jesus followers to co-labor with Him for His purposes and His glory.

Pause together with a partner or small group:

- Sharing your personal "born again" stories

- Celebrating that His Spirit, like the wind blows where it will bringing the new birth to all kinds of people, some like Nicodemus (and possibly you), the most unlikely

- Praying for one another that your walk with Jesus would experience the freedom to be characterized less by the "natural" and more by the "supernatural"

Walking in the Light of God's Son

Through Fresh Encounters With Jesus   John 12:35; John 8:12

"For this is how much God loved the world—he gave his one and only, unique Son as a gift. So now everyone who believes in him will never perish but experience everlasting life" (John 3:16).

W6

Encountering Jesus in the Word for deepened transformation in Christ-likeness

The Startling Love of Jesus

Possibly the most familiar of all Bible verses is about a God who loves. How startling it is when we begin to imagine the wonder of such love, the miracle of the gift, named Jesus!

All across the pages of Scripture, we're touched by the uniqueness of the God-man Jesus.

Christ's words were startling and His miracles amazing, but everything He said and did was meant to call attention to how He loved. Take a moment now to reflect on how Jesus loved people and how He startled them with His love.

Jesus startled lepers by healing their bodies and bringing dignity to their lives, sometimes even touching them in order to heal them (Luke 5:12,13; 17:11–19).

Christ startled a Samaritan woman when He broke all cultural conventions by asking her for a drink of water. In the midst of her shame and rejection, the Savior entrusted her with a conversation about eternal things (John 4:4–26).

Jesus startled the woman caught in adultery when He knelt down beside her, joining her at the point of her hurt, and providing protection for her life. He dispersed her accusers with His words and then offered restoration to her as He lovingly said, "Dear woman, where are your accusers? Is there no one here to condemn you?"Looking around, she replied, "I see no one, Lord." Jesus said, "Then I certainly don't condemn you either. Go, and from now on, be free from a life of sin" (John 8:10–11).

Pause now and reflect on the startling love of Jesus:

Jesus, you first startled me with love as you brought me into relationship with you. Pause to give Him thanks. "Dear Lord, I give you thanks for loving me to yourself when . . ."

Jesus, do it again; keep it up! "Dear Lord, open the eyes of my heart that I may not miss the abundance and constancy of your startling love."

Walking in the Light of God's Word

Through Frequent Experience of Scripture   John 12:35; Psalm 119:105

"So it's necessary for him to increase and for me to be diminished" (John 3:30).

Encountering Jesus in the Word for deepened transformation in Christ-likeness

From this significant discourse, we find a critical imperative to living a life of personal revival, contributing salt and light in the daily traffic patterns of life. It is a two-dimensional imperative: HE must increase, and I must decrease!

The imperative is not just for John the baptizer, but for each Spirit-empowered follower. Practically, *what does it look like* for Jesus to gain preeminence? Think about your daily living, your thoughts and activities, your attitudes and priorities.

Scripture reminds us that:

- His THOUGHTS are higher than yours (Isaiah 55:8).

- His ACTIVITY is characterized by the fruit of the Spirit, and never the deeds of the flesh (Galatians 5:19–24).

- His ATTITUDE is characterized by humility and thinking more highly of others (Philippians 2:3–7).

- His PRIORITIES focus on loving His Father, loving people, and imparting the gospel that others might embrace His and these priorities (Matthew 22:37–40, 28:19–20).

For Him to increase and me to decrease will impact all of life, my thoughts and activities, my attitudes and priorities. Living out this one Bible verse gives a powerful but simple goal for each day—let Jesus increase!

A lifestyle of revival and following Jesus is characterized by living John 3:30 each day with evidences of His thinking and activity, His attitude and priorities.

Pause to reflect and celebrate recent evidence of Him "increasing":

I recently was having more of HIS thoughts as I _____.

Recently, in my daily activity, I sensed the fruit of His Spirit when _____ _____.

His attitude of humility and thinking first of others was evident recently as I _____.

His priority of love toward Him and others was expressed recently when _____.

His priority of sharing my life and the gospel was recently demonstrated as I _____.

Celebrate one or more of these evidences of Him "increasing," and then pray for one another that these changes would continue as you "decrease."

THE BOOK OF JOHN is a long, inspired, passionately outsourced book trying to save us from evangelical rationalism, the doctrine that says the text is enough. Textual is as deadly as liberalism. A.W. Tozer, *God Still Speaks: Are We Listening?*

SPIRIT
EMPOWERED
Faith

W6

Encountering Jesus in the Word for deepened transformation in Christ-likeness

John 4

...and love your neighbor as you love yourself. The whole law and the prophets depend on these two commandments" (Matthew 22:37–40 NASB).

REREAD JOHN 4 EACH DAY REFLECTING ON A DIFFERENT ASPECT OF HIS LOVE.

DAY 1

L3

Experiencing God as He really is through deepened intimacy with Him

I. **Reflect on how the REAL God is a God of love.** How might this text lead me to better love God? "We love because He first loved us" (1 John 4:19 NASB). We can only love the REAL God with all our "heart, soul, mind, and strength."

A. As you read and reflect on the chapter, how might you describe the REAL God as He is seen as Father, Son, and Holy Spirit?

1. In verse_____, He is seen as _____
   _____.

2. In verse _____, He is seen as _____
   _____.

3. In verse _____, the love of Jesus is seen toward_____
   as He _____.

4. In verse _____, the love of Jesus is seen toward_____
   as He _____.

5. How might these insights challenge some of your misconceptions of God?

   Sadly, I sometimes mistakenly see God as _____
   _____.

DAY 2

W1

Frequently being led by the Spirit into deeper love for the One who wrote the Word

B. **Reflect on how God has loved *you*** since He is the same yesterday, today, and forever (Hebrews 13:8). **Pause to let Him love you.**

1. *Father, as you express yourself to me as the God who* _____
   _____, *my heart is moved with*
   _____.

2. *Father, as you express yourself to me as the God who* _____
   _____, *my heart is moved with*
   _____.

C. Jesus is available to love you like we read of His love in this chapter. Pause to express your heart to Him as you see Him in this chapter.

1. Describe how Jesus has loved you in some of the same ways that you read of His love in this chapter:

   I have experienced the love of Jesus as He has _____
   _____.

2. *Jesus, as you love me like you loved those in this chapter, my heart is touched with* _____.

DAY 3

P5

Ministering His life and love to our nearest ones at home and with family as well as faithful engagement in His body, the church

II. **Reflect on how you can better love your "near ones."** How might this text lead me to better love others? "As I have loved you, so you also should love one another." (John 13:34 NASB).

Since we have freely received of His love, we are to freely give this same love to others. Consider again how you see love portrayed in this chapter.

A. Who among your family or friends might you better love?

1. *I could better love_____,*
   especially by _____.

DAY 4

M1

Imparting the gospel and one's very life in daily activities and relationships, vocation and community

B. **Reflect on how you might be a witness of His love.** Notice again how Jesus expressed love by accepting, forgiving, or sacrificing? How might Jesus have taken initiative, expressed compassion, offered support, shared truth, and eternal hope?

1. Who in the traffic patterns of your life might benefit from receiving the blessing of Christ's love through you?
   (Who)_____could benefit from my sharing the love of Jesus by _____.

2. Who in your life could benefit from sharing part of your life story of encountering truth and eternal hope?
   (Who)_____could benefit from my sharing more of
   _____.

3. Pause now to pray for this person and then for yourself as you impart both your life and the gospel.

DAY 5

L4

Rejoicing regularly in my identity as "His Beloved"

III. **Reflect on *you* as the recipient of His love.** Your significance, value, and worth have been established by your Creator through the gift of His Son. How might this text affirm your identity as "His Beloved"?

"The light of God's love shined within us when he sent his matchless Son into the world so that we might live through him." (1 John 4:9).

Celebrate how you have received His love and grace, His forgiveness and new life, His calling and kingdom purpose.

A. Reread the text as His truth being shared just for you.

1. *I'm grateful that I have experienced the blessing of verse _____*
   as I _____.

B. Since He is the same yesterday, today, and forever, meditate on your being *in* the story of this chapter. Allow Him to love you as you read of His love in the chapter.

1. *My heart is touched with gratitude that Jesus _____*
   _____.

Walking in the Light of God's Son

Through Fresh Encounters With Jesus   John 12:35; John 8:12

"Jesus said to her, 'You don't have to wait any longer, the Anointed One is here speaking with you—I am the One you're looking for'" (John 4:26).

L5

Living with a passionate longing for purity and to please Him in all things

Shockingly, Jesus revealed to the Samaritan woman that He was the Messiah, but how did she deserve or merit such revelation? It was only by grace, unmerited, and so it is with you and me.

Reflect on what you have done or could do to deserve His forgiveness. There's *nothing* that you could do to earn the gift of His Son? Every one of us must conclude: It's only by His grace. Only God's unconditional love provided the gift of Calvary and the forgiveness that is available to us.

Make a list of all the things you have done this week to cause God to love you *less*:

_____

_____

_____

Answer: NOTHING!

Make a list of all the things you have done this week to cause God to love you *more*:

_____

_____

_____

Answer: NOTHING!

"For it was always in his perfect plan to adopt us as his delightful children, through our union with Jesus, the Anointed One, so that his tremendous love that cascades over us would glorify his grace —for the same love he has for his Beloved One, Jesus, he has for us. And this unfolding plan brings him great pleasure!" (Ephesians 1:6).

Now allow the Holy Spirit to touch your heart with thanks and gratitude, praise and wonder, that God has freely given the gift of His Son and the empowering of His Spirit.

Share your praise and worship with the Lord:

Father, as I consider the unmerited gift and provision of your Son and your Spirit just for me, my heart is touched with _____.

Overwhelm me with gratitude and empower me through the wonder of your grace that I might live life pleasing you in all things.

Walking in the Light of God's Word

Through Frequent Experience of Scripture   John 12:35; Psalm 119:105

"My food is to be doing the will of him who sent me and bring it to completion" (John 4:34).

L5

Living with a passionate longing for purity and to please Him in all things

nsights from how Jesus responded to the Father point to one critical factor—YIELD! We don't quarrel; we yield (see Isaiah 45:9). Nowhere in Scripture do we see the Father yielding to the Son. Indeed, the Father is always the one who commands, sends, and commissions the Son. The Son, as a demonstration of His love, always yields to the Father. Jesus' commitment to yield was so strong that He described it as His very nourishment.

Consider the following additional statements of Jesus from the gospel of John:

"I do not seek my own will, but the will of Him who sent me" (John 5:30 NASB).

"I love the Father and… I do exactly what my Father has commanded me" (John 14:31 NASB).

"If you obey my commands, you will remain in my love, just as I have obeyed my Father's commands and remain in his love" (John 15:10).

One of the ways we express love to the Father is to yield to His will and to His ways for our life. Great love is expressed when we yield, even before we know His exact plans for us. Our fulfillment of what Jesus called the Greatest Commandment (Matthew 22:37–40)—to love God—includes the discipline of yielding! One of the simplest ways to love God is to say, "Yes Lord! Now what would you have me do?"

Consider pausing in a prayer of yielding:

Lord, I acknowledge your work in my life and yield to it. Continue your Spirit's work in me that I might better express the life and love of Jesus.

Walking in the Light of God's People

Through Faithful Engagement in Fellowship   John 12:35; Matthew 5:14

"'Your son will live and not die.' So from that day forward, the man and all his family and servants believed" (John 4:53).

SPIRIT EMPOWERED *Faith*

L5

Living with a passionate longing for purity and to please Him in all things

Just like this Samaritan father, great things happen as we encounter Jesus, walking by faith in His Word.

Reflect upon the time when you first entered into relationship with the Savior. Do you remember really desiring to please Him, to put a smile on His face, so to speak? Was a longing to please Jesus part of your "new birth" experience?

When you think back on this time, did you desire to:

- Put away certain things, attitudes, or behaviors from your life?
- Avoid certain familiar patterns and places?
- Flee certain activities and acquaintances?
- Meditate upon God's Word?
- Worship with fellow Christ-followers?
- Share your experiences with Jesus with other people?

Complete as many of these sentences as you can:

As I think back upon my experience of accepting Jesus as my Savior, I recall these thoughts of wanting to please Him:

_____

_____

_____

_____

_____.

"…to live in a manner worthy of the Lord, so as to be fully pleasing, in every good work bearing fruit…" (Colossians 1:10 NASB).

Lord Jesus, I desire to please you, to "walk worthy" of my calling. I dread displeasing you and I sense the Holy Spirit touching my heart, giving me a deeper motivation to yield to you in these ways:

_____

_____

_____

_____

_____.

My Journal

L5

Living with a passionate longing for purity and to please Him in all things

John 5

…and love your neighbor as you love yourself. The whole law and the prophets depend on these two commandments" (Matthew 22:37–40 NASB).

REREAD JOHN 5 EACH DAY REFLECTING ON A DIFFERENT ASPECT OF HIS LOVE.

DAY 1

L3

Experiencing God as He really is through deepened intimacy with Him

I. **Reflect on how the REAL God is a God of love.** How might this text lead me to better love God? "We love because He first loved us" (1 John 4:19 NASB). We can only love the REAL God with all our "heart, soul, mind, and strength."

A. As you read and reflect on the chapter, how might you describe the REAL God as He is seen as Father, Son, and Holy Spirit?

1. In verse_____, He is seen as _____
_____.

2. In verse _____, He is seen as _____
_____.

3. In verse _____, the love of Jesus is seen toward_____
as He _____.

4. In verse _____, the love of Jesus is seen toward_____
as He _____.

5. How might these insights challenge some of your misconceptions of God?

Sadly, I sometimes mistakenly see God as _____
_____.

DAY 2

W1

Frequently being led by the Spirit into deeper love for the One who wrote the Word

B. **Reflect on how God has loved *you* since He is the same yesterday, today, and forever (Hebrews 13:8). Pause to let Him love you.**

1. *Father, as you express yourself to me as the God who* _____
_____, *my heart is moved with*
_____.

2. *Father, as you express yourself to me as the God who* _____
_____, *my heart is moved with*
_____.

C. Jesus is available to love you like we read of His love in this chapter. Pause to express your heart to Him as you see Him in this chapter.

1. Describe how Jesus has loved you in some of the same ways that you read of His love in this chapter:

I have experienced the love of Jesus as He has _____
_____.

2. *Jesus, as you love me like you loved those in this chapter, my heart is touched with* _____.

DAY 3

P5

Ministering His life and love to our nearest ones at home and with family as well as faithful engagement in His body, the church

II. **Reflect on how you can better love your "near ones."** How might this text lead me to better love others? "As I have loved you, so you also should love one another." (John 13:34 NASB).

Since we have freely received of His love, we are to freely give this same love to others. Consider again how you see love portrayed in this chapter.

A. Who among your family or friends might you better love?

1. *I could better love_____,*
   especially by _____.

DAY 4

M1

Imparting the gospel and one's very life in daily activities and relationships, vocation and community

B. **Reflect on how you might be a witness of His love.** Notice again how Jesus expressed love by accepting, forgiving, or sacrificing? How might Jesus have taken initiative, expressed compassion, offered support, shared truth, and eternal hope?

1. Who in the traffic patterns of your life might benefit from receiving the blessing of Christ's love through you?
   (Who)_____could benefit from my sharing the love
   of Jesus by _____.

2. Who in your life could benefit from sharing part of your life story of encountering truth and eternal hope?
   (Who)_____could benefit from my sharing more of
   _____

3. Pause now to pray for this person and then for yourself as you impart both your life and the gospel.

DAY 5

L4

Rejoicing regularly in my identity as "His Beloved"

III. **Reflect on *you* as the recipient of His love.** Your significance, value, and worth have been established by your Creator through the gift of His Son. How might this text affirm your identity as "His Beloved"?

"The light of God's love shined within us when he sent his matchless Son into the world so that we might live through him." (1 John 4:9).

Celebrate how you have received His love and grace, His forgiveness and new life, His calling and kingdom purpose.

A. Reread the text as His truth being shared just for you.

1. *I'm grateful that I have experienced the blessing of verse _____*
   as I _____.

B. Since He is the same yesterday, today, and forever, meditate on your being *in* the story of this chapter. Allow Him to love you as you read of His love in the chapter.

1. *My heart is touched with gratitude that Jesus _____*
   _____

Walking in the Light of God's Son

Through Fresh Encounters With Jesus   John 12:35; John 8:12

"When Jesus saw him lying there, he knew that the man had been crippled for a long time. So Jesus said to him, 'Do you truly long to be healed?'" (John 5:6).

L 10

Practicing the presence of the Lord, yielding to the Spirit's work of Christ-likeness

Imagine a place where healing waters were stirred by grace but limited by man's ability to be first in line—a place where deliverance had gained a reputation but only for the fastest, not the neediest or the most downtrodden?

That is where you find Jesus. See Him standing, observing, talking, listening. He is asking the Father, "What do you want me to do?"

There is a man lying near the pool. He is a nobody in a beautiful place, but he is marred by the worst that life can offer. Jesus stands over him. "Excuse me, sir, but do you truly long to be healed?" There is no demand, only as honest of a question that could be asked. "Do you want the impossible… Do you want the improbable…Do you want what you have asked God for every day…Are you ready to have your life changed?"

The man doesn't answer the question, at least not directly. In fact, his response is that healing is impossible. Not improbable or unlikely. Impossible! For some, even though they are lying every day in a beautiful place, their only identity is the sin and sickness they have come to know.

Take a moment to encounter Jesus beside your own troubled waters. Hear Him ask the question, "What do you want Me to do?" Tell Him now, and He promises to take it before the Father!

He is not bound by what you believe about yourself. He is not waiting for you to get the right answer to the question. He knows you do not have the strength or even the belief. In fact, that's the very reason He is asking the question. **He stirs the waters of the soul.** He troubles the heart and mind so that His miracle of transformation can take root and thrive.

Next, move towards the place you desire to be. Jesus told the man, "Get up!"

Now speak up with gratitude that demonstrates faith.

Pray like this…

Jesus, thank you that you hear me! I yield to your grace and lean into your mercy. I receive by faith the promise and power of your Holy Spirit. You have met me beside these troubled waters, and now I give you praise.

What is the lesson? Jesus is at His best when you are at your worst. So welcome to the springs of living water, which will empower your victorious living. His name is Jesus.

Walking in the Light of God's People

"Every day my Father is at work, and I will be too!" (John 5:17).

Never alone . . . That is the message from Genesis through Revelation. God, the triune God, is never alone. When Jesus came to earth, He was sent by the Father. As Jesus walked the earth, He only did what He saw and heard from heaven. His leaving was so the Holy Spirit could come. Like a beloved son whose passion is to work alongside his dad, Jesus' work on earth was the perfect reflection of all that the Father did and would do. There is a joy in Jesus' words, "I am at work too!"

So it should be in the church. Many in the church try to do what is the task of the Holy Spirit instead of doing what they are uniquely called to do. This begs the question; what is God asking you to do?

Imagine a work site where plumbers, electricians, and carpenters are all at work. Each of them has a specific assigned task. As a result, what was an empty construction site becomes exactly what the architect designed.

The Father is the divine architect of His kingdom on earth. Jesus is the Construction Supervisor, and the Holy Spirit is the Power Source. Ephesians 4:8 says "He gave gifts to his people." Everyone has a job to do, and that job is a delight to the Father, the Son, and the Holy Spirit.

Meditate on Ephesians 1:18–19 and be encouraged! You are called to the same thing the Father is doing in heaven. "I pray that the light of God will illuminate the eyes of your imagination, flooding you with light, until you experience the full revelation of the hope of his calling—that is, the wealth of God's glorious inheritances that he finds in us, his holy ones! I pray that you will continually experience the immeasurable greatness of God's power made available to you through faith. Then your lives will be an advertisement of this immense power as it works through you!".

The goal of every calling is to do what Jesus did, which is to come alongside others at their own point of need. As Jesus removed the aloneness of the man at the pool of Bethesda, every ministry the church is to do results in the same. Whether it is evangelism, practical support, caring for widows and orphans, church planting, or preaching, every task is meant to remove the terrible curse of separation that sin birthed in the garden of Eden.

Here's what to do. In very simple words, write down what God has called you to do. Ask the question, "What am I equipped to do?"

Then with your small group or partner, pray and ask the Father to empower you to do what He has uniquely designed you to do. **Pray like this:**

Father, thank you that you have uniquely designed me to work in your kingdom. Free me from seeking to do what you've called others to do. I accept your calling to _____.

Please send your Holy Spirit to open my eyes so that I can see your purposes and fulfill my calling in your church.

SPIRIT EMPOWERED
Faith
L 10

Practicing the presence of the Lord, yielding to the Spirit's work of Christ-likeness

Walking in the Light of God's Word

Through Frequent Experience of Scripture   John 12:35; Psalm 119:105

"I speak to you timeless truth. The Son is not able to do anything from himself or through my own initiative. I only do the works that I see the Father doing, for the Son does the same works as his Father" (John 5:19).

L10

Practicing the presence of the Lord, yielding to the Spirit's work of Christ-likeness

magine that you are one of the twelve disciples. You have left everything to follow Jesus, entrusting your life and future to this Carpenter from Nazareth. Your hopes are riding on an unclear vision of His plans for a "kingdom." It is becoming increasingly clear that the Jewish leaders are not big fans of His. In fact, they are trying to kill Him, and maybe you too!

Now imagine your reaction as you hear Jesus say: "the Son can do nothing of Himself." Are you surprised by this declaration of humble dependence? Surely this One whom you are following has some kind of plan, right? Doesn't He enjoy some sense of security about the future? Are you a bit shocked when you hear Him say, in essence, "I just wait around for the Father to show Me what to do"?

Jesus' words, startling though they may be, provide the blueprint for our lives. We are called to express humility through complete dependence upon God and His Word. Faithful, maturing disciples who walk intimately with the Spirit are able to declare, as Christ did, "I cannot do anything on my own" (John 5:30 NASB).

Too often the bible is read like a newspaper that describes everything that is going on while the reader remains unengaged, satisfied to have the information without ever experiencing the flesh and blood of engagement.

The man at the pool of Bethesda heard the word, engaged the command, and experienced the love of God when he took the chance to stand and walk. Had he not acted on the Word, he would not have experienced the healing power of God.

How do you need to experience the written word today? What step is the Father encouraging you to take? Pray like this:

"Father, as I read your word I recognize that you always meet your children exactly where they are…You have come to me, Father, and now I come to you! Today, I want to experience your grace by…" (Sharing your word, walking away from sin, practicing the fruit of your Spirit, etc.)

As you read His Word each day, ask the Holy Spirit to speak to you.

Write down what you sense He is telling you. **Pray and thank the Holy Spirit** that He goes with you and before you. Trust that our adequacy is in Him and His Word. Now go and live each day experiencing the Father's love through His Word.

L 10

Practicing the presence
of the Lord, yielding
to the Spirit's work of
Christ-likeness

John 6

...and love your neighbor as you love yourself. The whole law and the prophets depend on these two commandments" (Matthew 22:37–40 NASB).

REREAD JOHN 6 EACH DAY REFLECTING ON A DIFFERENT ASPECT OF HIS LOVE.

DAY 1

L3

Experiencing God as He really is through deepened intimacy with Him

I. **Reflect on how the REAL God is a God of love.** How might this text lead me to better love God? "We love because He first loved us" (1 John 4:19 NASB). We can only love the REAL God with all our "heart, soul, mind, and strength."

A. As you read and reflect on the chapter, how might you describe the REAL God as He is seen as Father, Son, and Holy Spirit?

1. In verse _____, He is seen as _____
   _____.

2. In verse _____, He is seen as _____
   _____.

3. In verse _____, the love of Jesus is seen toward_____
   as He _____.

4. In verse _____, the love of Jesus is seen toward_____
   as He _____.

5. How might these insights challenge some of your misconceptions of God?

   Sadly, I sometimes mistakenly see God as _____
   _____.

DAY 2

W1

Frequently being led by the Spirit into deeper love for the One who wrote the Word

B. **Reflect on how God has loved *you*** since He is the same yesterday, today, and forever (Hebrews 13:8). **Pause to let Him love you.**

1. *Father, as you express yourself to me as the God who* _____
   _____, *my heart is moved with*
   _____.

2. *Father, as you express yourself to me as the God who* _____
   _____, *my heart is moved with*
   _____.

C. Jesus is available to love you like we read of His love in this chapter. Pause to express your heart to Him as you see Him in this chapter.

1. Describe how Jesus has loved you in some of the same ways that you read of His love in this chapter:

   I have experienced the love of Jesus as He has _____
   _____.

2. *Jesus, as you love me like you loved those in this chapter, my heart is touched with* _____.

DAY 3

P5

Ministering His life and love to our nearest ones at home and with family as well as faithful engagement in His body, the church

II. **Reflect on how you can better love your "near ones."** How might this text lead me to better love others? "As I have loved you, so you also should love one another." (John 13:34 NASB).

Since we have freely received of His love, we are to freely give this same love to others. Consider again how you see love portrayed in this chapter.

A. Who among your family or friends might you better love?

1. *I could better love_____,*
   especially by _____.

DAY 4

M1

Imparting the gospel and one's very life in daily activities and relationships, vocation and community

B. **Reflect on how you might be a witness of His love.** Notice again how Jesus expressed love by accepting, forgiving, or sacrificing? How might Jesus have taken initiative, expressed compassion, offered support, shared truth, and eternal hope?

1. Who in the traffic patterns of your life might benefit from receiving the blessing of Christ's love through you?
   (Who)_____could benefit from my sharing the love
   of Jesus by _____.

2. Who in your life could benefit from sharing part of your life story of encountering truth and eternal hope?
   (Who)_____could benefit from my sharing more of
   _____

3. Pause now to pray for this person and then for yourself as you impart both your life and the gospel.

DAY 5

L4

Rejoicing regularly in my identity as "His Beloved"

III. **Reflect on *you* as the recipient of His love.** Your significance, value, and worth have been established by your Creator through the gift of His Son. How might this text affirm your identity as "His Beloved"?

"The light of God's love shined within us when he sent his matchless Son into the world so that we might live through him." (1 John 4:9).

Celebrate how you have received His love and grace, His forgiveness and new life, His calling and kingdom purpose.

A. Reread the text as His truth being shared just for you.

1. *I'm grateful that I have experienced the blessing of verse _____*
   as I _____.

B. Since He is the same yesterday, today, and forever, meditate on your being *in* the story of this chapter. Allow Him to love you as you read of His love in the chapter.

1. *My heart is touched with gratitude that Jesus _____*
   _____

Walking in the Light of God's Son

Through Fresh Encounters With Jesus   John 12:35; John 8:12

"Here's a young person with five barley loaves and two small fish" (John 6:9).

"Jesus then took the barley loaves and the fish and gave thanks to God. He then gave it to the disciples to distribute to the people. Miraculously, the food multiplied, with everyone eating as much as they wanted!" (John 6:11).

SPIRIT EMPOWERED
Faith

L10

Practicing the presence of the Lord, yielding to the Spirit's work of Christ-likeness

There is no better illustration of "freely receiving" and "freely giving" of His provision than Christ's miracle of feeding thousands. "Freely you received, freely give" (Matthew 10:8 NASB).

Pause quietly to picture Christ with eyes toward heaven, His hands open.

With one hand, He receives what is available—five loaves and two fish from a young lad.

With one hand, He gives freely and abundantly to the needs of all.

At times, this calling is to freely receive as He gives to you. At other times, He calls you to freely give to the needs of others. His inheritance toward you never runs out. His provision is without limit.

Quietly consider: What encouragement, care, support, or affirmation might you need in the midst of your struggles? Yield to the Holy Spirit within you. Would you open your heart to receive these gifts from Christ, the One who provides?

What acceptance, compassion, appreciation, or respect might you freely give to someone this week? Could you take the time to think of a specific name and then yield to the Spirit's prompting? As you share His life and love, others will find hope in the Jesus who provides.

Pray like this:

Lord Jesus, I sense that you would be pleased for me to share _____ _____ with_____.

Prompt and empower me to do so by your Spirit. We find hope in a Jesus who provides.

Walking in the Light of God's Word

Through Frequent Experience of Scripture 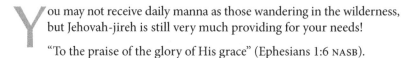   John 12:35; Psalm 119:105

"The bread of God is the One who came out of heaven to give his life to feed the world. 'Then please, sir, give us this bread every day'" (John 6:33–34).

M1

Imparting the gospel and one's very life in daily activities and relationships, vocation and community

You may not receive daily manna as those wandering in the wilderness, but Jehovah-jireh is still very much providing for your needs!

"To the praise of the glory of His grace" (Ephesians 1:6 NASB).

Pause to reflect upon your experience of the glory of God's grace, recently or in the past. Be still before the Lord and ask His Spirit to stir up remembrances, perhaps of times when:

- He unexpectedly provided for you.

- He accepted you in the midst of a failure.

- He healed your physical or emotional pain.

- He restored a broken relationship.

Complete the following sentence:

I give thanks and praise to God for the grace He gave me when _____
_____
_____
_____

Share your completed sentence with your partner or small group. Then **pray together,** expressing further thanks and praise to God as your grateful heart is prompted to give abundantly to others.

Walking in the Light of God's People

Through Faithful Engagement in Fellowship John 12:35; Matthew 5:14

"When the Jews who were hostile to Jesus heard him say, 'I am the bread that came down from heaven,' they immediately began to complain" (John 6:41).

M6

Bearing witness of a confident peace and expectant hope in God's Lordship in all things

Many today still grumble because they miss seeing Him for who He really is. Sadly, many miss Jesus because they don't encounter Him in His people.

Pause to ask God *who* in the traffic pattern of your life needs to experience encouragement, comfort, acceptance, or support through you!

"No one has ever gazed upon the fullness of God's splendor. But if we love one another, God makes his permanent home in us, and we make our permanent home in him, and his love is brought to its full expression in us" (1 John 4:12).

True fellowship, in which we genuinely love each other, enables the *full expression* of God's love. This means as we experience God's love through the love of others, we see Him as He really is. As we receive acceptance from others, we'll be able to see the God of gracious acceptance (Romans 15:7). Through the comfort of a friend, we'll be able to see the One who is "the Father of tender mercy and the God of endless comfort" (2 Corinthians 1:3).

Just as we receive this blessing of experiencing God through others, we are called to express His presence to others, giving testimony to His glorious riches in order that they might see Him more clearly and find added hope.

Pray together with a partner or small group, asking for His life to be shared through you, beginning with those close to you and with other followers of Jesus, and then extend this sharing of His love to others who need to know Him.

WHAT WAS IT LIKE? He was the old man who taught in the villages and homes in the miraculous chaos of the first century church. He was the last of the caretakers appointed by the Lord through the years of infancy of His church. He was the last of the apostles in the first century of new faith. He had suffered over and over at the cruel hands of the culture that he loved, but still they came. Seeking what he knew. Questioning, always questioning how he knew what he proclaimed to be true. And over and over he would tell the stories, give the lessons, his eyes glistening with tears as he remembered the events he could not forget. Those stories became his life, emblazoned by the fire of God that was never quenched in the soul of the man who would never forget. Finally, they were written…his story of The Story, the gospel according to the beloved disciple, John.

SPIRIT
EMPOWERED
Faith

M6

Bearing witness of a confident peace and expectant hope in God's Lordship in all things

John 7

…and love your neighbor as you love yourself. The whole law and the prophets depend on these two commandments" (Matthew 22:37–40 NASB).

REREAD JOHN 7 EACH DAY REFLECTING ON A DIFFERENT ASPECT OF HIS LOVE.

DAY 1

SPIRIT
EMPOWERED
Faith

L3

Experiencing God as He really is through deepened intimacy with Him

I. **Reflect on how the REAL God is a God of love.** How might this text lead me to better love God? "We love because He first loved us" (1 John 4:19 NASB). We can only love the REAL God with all our "heart, soul, mind, and strength."

A. As you read and reflect on the chapter, how might you describe the REAL God as He is seen as Father, Son, and Holy Spirit?

1. In verse_____, He is seen as _____
   _____.

2. In verse _____, He is seen as _____
   _____.

3. In verse _____, the love of Jesus is seen toward_____
   as He _____.

4. In verse _____, the love of Jesus is seen toward_____
   as He _____.

5. How might these insights challenge some of your misconceptions of God?

   Sadly, I sometimes mistakenly see God as _____
   _____.

DAY 2

SPIRIT
EMPOWERED
Faith

W1

Frequently being led by the Spirit into deeper love for the One who wrote the Word

B. **Reflect on how God has loved *you*** since He is the same yesterday, today, and forever (Hebrews 13:8). **Pause to let Him love you.**

1. *Father, as you express yourself to me as the God who* _____
   _____, *my heart is moved with*
   _____.

2. *Father, as you express yourself to me as the God who* _____
   _____, *my heart is moved with*
   _____.

C. Jesus is available to love you like we read of His love in this chapter. Pause to express your heart to Him as you see Him in this chapter.

1. Describe how Jesus has loved you in some of the same ways that you read of His love in this chapter:

   I have experienced the love of Jesus as He has _____
   _____.

2. *Jesus, as you love me like you loved those in this chapter, my heart is touched with* _____.

DAY 3

SPIRIT EMPOWERED
Faith
P5

Ministering His life and love to our nearest ones at home and with family as well as faithful engagement in His body, the church

II. **Reflect on how you can better love your "near ones."** How might this text lead me to better love others? "As I have loved you, so you also should love one another." (John 13:34 NASB).

Since we have freely received of His love, we are to freely give this same love to others. Consider again how you see love portrayed in this chapter.

A. Who among your family or friends might you better love?

1. *I could better love_____,*
   especially by _____.

DAY 4

SPIRIT EMPOWERED
Faith
M1

Imparting the gospel and one's very life in daily activities and relationships, vocation and community

B. **Reflect on how you might be a witness of His love.** Notice again how Jesus expressed love by accepting, forgiving, or sacrificing? How might Jesus have taken initiative, expressed compassion, offered support, shared truth, and eternal hope?

1. Who in the traffic patterns of your life might benefit from receiving the blessing of Christ's love through you?
   (Who)_____could benefit from my sharing the love of Jesus by _____.

2. Who in your life could benefit from sharing part of your life story of encountering truth and eternal hope?
   (Who)_____could benefit from my sharing more of
   _____.

3. Pause now to pray for this person and then for yourself as you impart both your life and the gospel.

DAY 5

SPIRIT EMPOWERED
Faith
L4

Rejoicing regularly in my identity as "His Beloved"

III. **Reflect on *you* as the recipient of His love.** Your significance, value, and worth have been established by your Creator through the gift of His Son. How might this text affirm your identity as "His Beloved"?

"The light of God's love shined within us when he sent his matchless Son into the world so that we might live through him." (1 John 4:9).

Celebrate how you have received His love and grace, His forgiveness and new life, His calling and kingdom purpose.

A. Reread the text as His truth being shared just for you.

1. *I'm grateful that I have experienced the blessing of verse _____*
   as I _____.

B. Since He is the same yesterday, today, and forever, meditate on your being *in* the story of this chapter. Allow Him to love you as you read of His love in the chapter.

1. *My heart is touched with gratitude that Jesus _____*
   _____.

Walking in the Light of God's Word

Through Frequent Experience of Scripture   John 12:35; Psalm 119:105

"If you want to test my teachings and discover where I received them, first be passionate to do God's will, and then you will be able to discern if my teachings are from the heart of God or from my own opinions" (John 7:17).

Listening to and hearing God for direction and discernment

Our commitment in faith to yield to God before we fully know Him is the secret to spiritual transformation. Like Jesus, we must say, "not as I will, but as you will" (Matthew 26:39 NASB). Are you committed to yield in this way? Is it your very "spiritual food" to do the Father's will (John 4:34)? We invite you, by faith, to pray a prayer of yielding— to give expression to your heart's commitment to yield to whatever God asks of you, even when you do not really understand what He is asking or what He is doing.

Consider the circumstances of your life right now. Think about your important relationships. Reflect upon critical situations and unanswered questions. What are you struggling with right now?

Compose your own prayer of commitment to yield, and then offer it to God. Use the structure below to assist you as needed.

Father, before I even hear your voice concerning…

- *My calling as a husband/wife/parent or friend to… (For example: my calling as a parent to demonstrate the importance of personal purity, regarding what I allow to come into my mind).*

- *The decision regarding…(For example: the decision regarding how to best care for our aging parents).*

- *How I should handle…(For example: how I should handle the conflict with my boss).*

- *What I should trust you for relative to…(For example: what I should trust you for relative to my health problem and the treatment for it)*

I yield to you all that I am and all that my future holds. By faith, I commit to live out what you reveal. Speak Lord, your servant listens.

After you have offered your prayer and spent some time listening for the Lord, **share your prayer with your partner or small group. Pray for one another,** asking God to answer your prayers and to empower each of you to live out your commitment to yield.

Walking in the Light of God's Son

Through Fresh Encounters With Jesus   John 12:35; John 8:12

"Believe in me, so that rivers of living water will burst out from within you; flowing from your innermost being" (John 7:38).

Quietly meditate on the invitation of Jesus. Come to Him. He has available the Holy Spirit's presence and power for you.

"Jesus was prophesying about the Holy Spirit that believers were being prepared to receive. But the Holy Spirit had not yet been poured out upon them, because Jesus had not yet been unveiled in his full splendor" (John 7:39).

The Holy Spirit is the One who provides discernment and direction as we pause to yield to His fullness.

Respond to His promise of the Spirit flowing through you. Welcome the Holy Spirit's prompting and empowerment. Thank the Lord Jesus for not leaving you as an orphan, but coming to you through His Spirit. You are never alone as He guides, directs, and empowers.

SPIRIT EMPOWERED *Faith*

L2

Listening to and hearing God for direction and discernment

Walking in the Light of God's People

Through Faithful Engagement in Fellowship   John 12:35; Matthew 5:14

"You don't understand—
he speaks amazing things like no one else has ever spoken"
(John 7:46).

The Lord…takes the upright into his confidence (Proverbs 3:32 NIV).

Consider a time in your life when you sensed God revealing something to you—when you felt that He "took you into His confidence." It may have occurred as you encountered Scripture, as you were praying or as you listened to the sharing of another. Then complete the following sentence, either on your own or using one of the sample beginnings listed below.

I remember having a very personal encounter with God when He…

- Drew me to Himself by…

- Gave specific direction concerning…

- Provided caution/warning about…

- Revealed Himself as…

- Confronted me concerning…

- Affirmed/encouraged me concerning…

- Reassured me during…

(For example: "I remember having a very personal encounter with God when He encouraged me concerning my worth to Him. I felt like a failure, but I sensed the Lord saying to me, 'I love you. Don't give up; trust Me.'")

"Discover creative ways to encourage others and to motivate them toward acts of compassion, doing beautiful works as expressions of love" (Hebrews 10:24).

SPIRIT EMPOWERED *Faith*
L2

Listening to and hearing God for direction and discernment

Listening to and hearing
God for direction and
discernment

John 8

...and love your neighbor as you love yourself. The whole law and the prophets depend on these two commandments" (Matthew 22:37–40 NASB).

REREAD JOHN 8 EACH DAY REFLECTING ON A DIFFERENT ASPECT OF HIS LOVE.

DAY 1

SPIRIT EMPOWERED
Faith

L3

Experiencing God as He really is through deepened intimacy with Him

I.   **Reflect on how the REAL God is a God of love.** How might this text lead me to better love God? "We love because He first loved us" (1 John 4:19 NASB). We can only love the REAL God with all our "heart, soul, mind, and strength."

A.   As you read and reflect on the chapter, how might you describe the REAL God as He is seen as Father, Son, and Holy Spirit?

1.   In verse_____, He is seen as _____
_____.

2.   In verse _____, He is seen as _____
_____.

3.   In verse _____ , the love of Jesus is seen toward_____
as He _____.

4.   In verse _____ , the love of Jesus is seen toward_____
as He _____.

5.   How might these insights challenge some of your misconceptions of God?

Sadly, I sometimes mistakenly see God as _____
_____.

DAY 2

SPIRIT EMPOWERED
Faith

W1

Frequently being led by the Spirit into deeper love for the One who wrote the Word

B.   **Reflect on how God has loved *you*** since He is the same yesterday, today, and forever (Hebrews 13:8). **Pause to let Him love you.**

1.   *Father, as you express yourself to me as the God who* _____
_____, *my heart is moved with*
_____.

2.   *Father, as you express yourself to me as the God who* _____
_____, *my heart is moved with*
_____.

C.   Jesus is available to love you like we read of His love in this chapter. Pause to express your heart to Him as you see Him in this chapter.

1.   Describe how Jesus has loved you in some of the same ways that you read of His love in this chapter:

I have experienced the love of Jesus as He has _____
_____.

2.   *Jesus, as you love me like you loved those in this chapter, my heart is touched with* _____.

DAY 3

SPIRIT EMPOWERED Faith

P5

Ministering His life and love to our nearest ones at home and with family as well as faithful engagement in His body, the church

II. **Reflect on how you can better love your "near ones."** How might this text lead me to better love others? "As I have loved you, so you also should love one another." (John 13:34 NASB).

Since we have freely received of His love, we are to freely give this same love to others. Consider again how you see love portrayed in this chapter.

A. Who among your family or friends might you better love?

1. *I could better love_____,*
   especially by _____.

DAY 4

SPIRIT EMPOWERED Faith

M1

Imparting the gospel and one's very life in daily activities and relationships, vocation and community

B. **Reflect on how you might be a witness of His love.** Notice again how Jesus expressed love by accepting, forgiving, or sacrificing? How might Jesus have taken initiative, expressed compassion, offered support, shared truth, and eternal hope?

1. Who in the traffic patterns of your life might benefit from receiving the blessing of Christ's love through you?
   (Who)_____could benefit from my sharing the love of Jesus by _____.

2. Who in your life could benefit from sharing part of your life story of encountering truth and eternal hope?
   (Who)_____could benefit from my sharing more of
   _____.

3. Pause now to pray for this person and then for yourself as you impart both your life and the gospel.

DAY 5

SPIRIT EMPOWERED Faith

L4

Rejoicing regularly in my identity as "His Beloved"

III. **Reflect on *you* as the recipient of His love.** Your significance, value, and worth have been established by your Creator through the gift of His Son. How might this text affirm your identity as "His Beloved"?

"The light of God's love shined within us when he sent his matchless Son into the world so that we might live through him." (1 John 4:9).

Celebrate how you have received His love and grace, His forgiveness and new life, His calling and kingdom purpose.

A. Reread the text as His truth being shared just for you.

1. *I'm grateful that I have experienced the blessing of verse _____*
   as I _____.

B. Since He is the same yesterday, today, and forever, meditate on your being *in* the story of this chapter. Allow Him to love you as you read of His love in the chapter.

1. *My heart is touched with gratitude that Jesus _____*
   _____.

Walking in the Light of God's People

Through Faithful Engagement in Fellowship   John 12:35; Matthew 5:14

"Then at dawn Jesus appeared in the temple courts again, and soon all the people gathered around to listen to his words, so he sat down and taught them" (John 8:2).

SPIRIT EMPOWERED
Faith

L4

Rejoicing regularly in my identity as "His Beloved"

I n John 8:1–11, Jesus demonstrates approachability, and others wish to gather around him. In our churches and fellowship together, let's create safe spaces around us in which people can experience Spirit-filled, life-changing fellowship.

A safe place to belong is characterized by…

▪ **Listening to and hearing the Words of Jesus:** "Then at dawn Jesus appeared in the temple courts again, and soon all the people gathered around to listen to his words, so he sat down and taught them" (John 8:2).

▪ **Welcoming *all* who join the group:** "Then in the middle of his teaching, the religious scholars and the Pharisees broke through the crowd and brought a woman who had been caught in the act of committing adultery and made her stand in the middle of everyone" (John 8:3).

▪ **Carefully handling questions** that are raised by participants: "Doesn't Moses' Law command us to stone to death a woman like this?" (John 8:5).

▪ **Boldly addressing emotions** that are present in the room: "Angry, they kept insisting that he answer their questions, so Jesus stood up and looked at them and said, 'Let's have the man who has never had a sinful desire throw the first stone at her'" (John 8:7).

▪ **Granting forgiveness** when appropriate: "I certainly don't condemn you either" (John 8:11).

Pause together and celebrate various ways that your fellowship is finding freedom from self-interest to become a safe place in which people can grow and change.

One of my favorite Jesus stories that we discussed and experienced recently was

_____.

I enjoy the diversity of our group as I'm a little different in that I _____

_____.

No question seems to be a "dumb" question here, and that makes me feel

_____.

No emotion seems to be "wrong" in this place, and I can tend to be _____

_____.

I have experienced forgiveness and grace through the people in this group by

_____.

Pray together, asking the Holy Spirit to continue to refine you and your community of Jesus followers: *"Dear Holy Spirit, refine our fellowship to be a 'safe space' for people to belong, believe, and become like Jesus."*

John 8   **45**

Walking in the Light of God's Son

Through Fresh Encounters With Jesus   John 12:35; John 8:12

"For I absolutely know who I am, where I've come from, and where I'm going" (John 8:14).

In John 8:12–30, Jesus asserts that He is the light of the world and not from this world. In His encounter with religious leaders, He speaks to His identify, background, and purpose, and offers hope to those of us who follow Him.

"For I absolutely know who I am, where I've come from, and where I'm going" (John 8:14).

"We are becoming more and more like Him, being jointly formed into His image" (Romans 8:29).

- **Who I am:** "Then Jesus said, 'I am light to the world and those who embrace me will experience life-giving light, and they will never walk in darkness'" (John 8:12). The religious leaders found their identity in religious performance. This is sometimes described as the religion of "who-do-ism," which occurs when who I *am* is equated with what I *do*.

- **Where I've come from:** "I am from above. I am not from this world…" (John 8:23). Jesus found security in the love of His Father.

- **Where I'm going:** "You will know me as 'I Am' after you have lifted me up from the earth as the Son of Man. Then you will realize that I do nothing on my own initiative, but I only speak the truth that the Father has revealed to me. I am his messenger and he is always with me, for I only do that which delights his heart" (John 8:28–29). Jesus defined His purpose in the context of a mutually dependent relationship with His Father—the Father reveals, and the Son of Man yields.

Pause and rejoice in your identity, creation, and purpose as a joint-heir of Jesus.

- Rejoicing in your identity as "His Beloved" (Song of Solomon 2:4; Ephesians 1:6)

- Celebrating how God has formed you and set you apart (Psalm 139:13; Jeremiah 1:5)

- Expressing appreciation for your purpose to do that which delights God's heart (Psalm 37:4)

Pray a prayer of gratitude for your identity, uniqueness, and purpose, allowing this joy to motivate all that you do and say as His follower:

Lord, I appreciate how you have designed me and called me to reflect your love to your people.

SPIRIT EMPOWERED
Faith

L4

Rejoicing regularly in my identity as "His Beloved"

Walking in the Light of God's Word

Through Frequent Experience of Scripture   John 12:35; Psalm 119:105

"Jesus said to those Jews who believed in him, 'When you continue to embrace all that I teach, you prove that you are my true followers. For if you embrace the truth, it will release more freedom into your lives" (John 8:31–32).

L4

Rejoicing regularly in my identity as "His Beloved"

I n John 8:31–59, Jesus offers encounters with His Word as a means to deepened transformation in Christ-likeness. Encountering Jesus in the Word transforms us to His likeness. This work of Christ-likeness through the Word includes the Holy Spirit's work of…

▪ **Self-awareness:** "Surprised by this, they said, 'But we're the descendants of Abraham and we're already free'" (John 8:33a). The Jews were unaware of their true spiritual condition. Experiencing the words of Jesus helps us to see ourselves as we are.

▪ **Humility:** "'We've never been in bondage to anyone. How could you say that we will be released into more freedom?'" (John 8:33b). Spiritual pride can hinder growth, but yielding to His truth can bring life change.

▪ **Faith:** "If you really knew God, you would listen, receive, and respond with faith to his words" (John 8:47). Being in relationship with the words of Christ brings about implicit, unwavering trust that they will never fail.

▪ **Gratitude:** "I have fully embraced him, and I treasure his every word" (John 8:55). The Jews took their relationship with God for granted. Gratitude will lead us into a deeper love for the one who spoke truth.

Pause and reflect on areas of potential growth and change that could lead to spiritual awakening in your life.

▪ **Ask the Lord for increased self-awareness:**
Dear Lord, please search me and help me to become aware of the areas that are hindering my spiritual maturity.

▪ **Ask a trusted friend for feedback:**
In our relationship, what do you need 'more of/less of' from me?

▪ **Ask a group member for prayer in areas of struggle:**
Would you please pray for me regarding…

▪ **Express thanksgiving to the Lord for a recent celebration:**
Lord, I appreciate how you recently…

Ask the Lord to establish in your life this one powerful daily discipline— "embrace the truth, it will release more freedom" (John 8:32):

Dear Lord Jesus, I desire to be teachable. Thank you for allowing me to embrace your truth, and help me to continue in that path.

Rejoicing regularly in my
identity as "His Beloved"

John 9

…and love your neighbor as you love yourself. The whole law and the prophets depend on these two commandments" (Matthew 22:37–40 NASB).

REREAD JOHN 9 EACH DAY REFLECTING ON A DIFFERENT ASPECT OF HIS LOVE.

DAY 1

L3

Experiencing God as He really is through deepened intimacy with Him

I. **Reflect on how the REAL God is a God of love.** How might this text lead me to better love God? "We love because He first loved us" (1 John 4:19 NASB). We can only love the REAL God with all our "heart, soul, mind, and strength."

A. As you read and reflect on the chapter, how might you describe the REAL God as He is seen as Father, Son, and Holy Spirit?

1. In verse_____, He is seen as _____
_____.

2. In verse _____, He is seen as _____
_____.

3. In verse _____ , the love of Jesus is seen toward_____
as He _____.

4. In verse _____ , the love of Jesus is seen toward_____
as He _____.

5. How might these insights challenge some of your misconceptions of God?

Sadly, I sometimes mistakenly see God as _____
_____.

DAY 2

W1

Frequently being led by the Spirit into deeper love for the One who wrote the Word

B. **Reflect on how God has loved *you*** since He is the same yesterday, today, and forever (Hebrews 13:8). **Pause to let Him love you.**

1. *Father, as you express yourself to me as the God who* _____
_____, *my heart is moved with*
_____.

2. *Father, as you express yourself to me as the God who* _____
_____, *my heart is moved with*
_____.

C. Jesus is available to love you like we read of His love in this chapter. Pause to express your heart to Him as you see Him in this chapter.

1. Describe how Jesus has loved you in some of the same ways that you read of His love in this chapter:

I have experienced the love of Jesus as He has _____
_____.

2. *Jesus, as you love me like you loved those in this chapter, my heart is touched with* _____.

DAY 3

Ministering His life and love to our nearest ones at home and with family as well as faithful engagement in His body, the church

II. Reflect on how you can better love your "near ones." How might this text lead me to better love others? "As I have loved you, so you also should love one another." (John 13:34 NASB).

Since we have freely received of His love, we are to freely give this same love to others. Consider again how you see love portrayed in this chapter.

A. Who among your family or friends might you better love?

1. *I could better love_____,*
   especially by _____.

DAY 4

Imparting the gospel and one's very life in daily activities and relationships, vocation and community

B. Reflect on how you might be a witness of His love. Notice again how Jesus expressed love by accepting, forgiving, or sacrificing? How might Jesus have taken initiative, expressed compassion, offered support, shared truth, and eternal hope?

1. Who in the traffic patterns of your life might benefit from receiving the blessing of Christ's love through you?
   (Who)_____could benefit from my sharing the love of Jesus by _____.

2. Who in your life could benefit from sharing part of your life story of encountering truth and eternal hope?
   (Who)_____could benefit from my sharing more of
   _____.

3. Pause now to pray for this person and then for yourself as you impart both your life and the gospel.

DAY 5

Rejoicing regularly in my identity as "His Beloved"

III. Reflect on *you* as the recipient of His love. Your significance, value, and worth have been established by your Creator through the gift of His Son. How might this text affirm your identity as "His Beloved"?

"The light of God's love shined within us when he sent his matchless Son into the world so that we might live through him." (1 John 4:9).

Celebrate how you have received His love and grace, His forgiveness and new life, His calling and kingdom purpose.

A. Reread the text as His truth being shared just for you.

1. *I'm grateful that I have experienced the blessing of verse _____*
   as I _____.

B. Since He is the same yesterday, today, and forever, meditate on your being *in* the story of this chapter. Allow Him to love you as you read of His love in the chapter.

1. *My heart is touched with gratitude that Jesus _____*
   _____.

Walking in the Light of God's Son

Through Fresh Encounters With Jesus John 12:35; John 8:12

"Teacher, whose sin caused this guy's blindness, his own, or sin of his parents?" Jesus answered, "Neither. It happened to him so that you could watch him experience God's miracle" (John 9:2–3).

M1

Imparting the gospel and one's very life in daily activities and relationships, vocation and community

Who sinned? The entire ninth chapter of John holds many great insights for the followers of Jesus. As Jesus and His disciples are going to Jerusalem, they come upon a man beside the road blind from birth. The Bible records that Jesus heals the man, subsequently prompting a lot of trouble. The man is called before the religious leaders. His family is brought in to try to explain what has happened to him. Finally, because he continues to testify that Jesus was responsible for his receiving his sight, they throw him out of the synagogue. When Jesus hears about it, He goes out, finds the man, and reveals more of Himself to him (see John 9:35).

Of specific importance to us becoming people who love as Jesus loved is the issue of grace. Surely He has looked beyond our faults to see our needs (Romans 5:8 and Luke 19:7), but can we do likewise?

One tragic part of the story is that even as Christ's heart is moved with compassion and grace, when the disciples looked at the same man beside the road, they asked this question, "Master, who sinned, this man or his parents . . ." Do you see the contrast between the heart of Jesus moved to minister to needs and the hearts of people and the disciples wanting to know, "who sinned"?

Following Jesus and loving as He loves means becoming a person of grace. It means seeing and ministering to needs, such as support, encouragement, and acceptance, rather than seeing and reacting only to behaviors. The power for sustaining a ministry to people in need must come from God and the power to give grace comes from having partaken of God's grace.

Walking in the Light of God's People

Through Faithful Engagement in Fellowship   John 12:35; Matthew 5:14

"When Jesus learned they had thrown him out, he went to find him and said to him, 'Do you believe in the Son of God?'" (John 9:35).

M1

Imparting the gospel and one's very life in daily activities and relationships, vocation and community

When Jesus learned they had thrown him out, he went to find him and said to him, 'Do you believe in the Son of God?'" (John 9:35).

This chapter describes the best day of this man's entire life, yet no one—not friends, family, or the religious community—was willing to celebrate with him. The people of the neighborhood ignored him. The religious leaders accused him. His family rejected him. But when Jesus heard all of this, He went to find him.

Has this ever happened to you? On one of the best or worse days of your life have you been left to either grieve or celebrate…alone?

Jesus gave the church a profound example to follow. Romans 12:15 says, "Rejoice with those who rejoice, and weep with those who weep."

Take a moment right now to recall a friend or loved one that is experiencing life alone. The Lord is calling you to simply walk alongside and encourage.

Pause with your small group or partner and ask God to "send" you:

Send me, Holy Spirit, to _____,
who at times is alone, struggling with _____.

Today, make a phone call, send a text, or have a cup of coffee and do what Jesus did. When He heard that the man was alone, His first response was not to preach to him, pray for him, or give a pep talk but simply to be *with* him.

Your friend needs the same today.

Walking in the Light of God's Word

Through Frequent Experience of Scripture   John 12:35; Psalm 119:105

"I have come to judge those who think they see and make them blind. And for those who are blind, I have come to make them see" (John 9:39)..

Like a map, God wrote the Scriptures to point to eternal life through Jesus. Yet, the religious elite of His day would not go down the path.

- They memorized, but it never went from the head to the heart.
- They acted out, but the words never changed their lives.
- They sought God but not the great gift of eternal life they said they pursued.

This is also true in the church today. There is much study but little sanctification. There are many translations but not much transformation. The words of Jesus are not only to be read, memorized, and sung about on Sunday morning, but experienced and practically walked out in daily life.

Get out of your head and into your heart. The Holy Spirit was given that we would never be alone (John 13:16–17). When we read His Word, the Holy Spirit is with us to direct us so the external word becomes the internal word that results in the directed path for life today.

Listen to His voice instead of just reading the words. Is there a path, a direction, or step that He is directing you to take today?

Pray and ask the Holy Spirit to speak to you from John 9, and then read the chapter. What Scripture has He impressed on your heart? Now verbalize the lesson back in prayer:

Lord, I see where you showed great grace to the blind man. I need that grace today…I see where many people ignored the man, but you sought him out… I see where the religious people read but never obeyed.

Now respond to what you "see" by doing what Jesus would do.

Read His words, listen to His voice, and experience the blessing of practical obedience in your life today:

Jesus, you promised that your Holy Spirit would lead me in all truth (John 16:13). I want to now be led in experiencing your truth. Today, allow your Word to go from my head to my heart. I commit to obey your instructions.

SPIRIT
EMPOWERED
Faith

M1

Imparting the gospel and one's very life in daily activities and relationships, vocation and community

ONE OF THE MOST READ BOOKS IN HISTORY IS THE BIBLE, which finds itself at the top of every list of best sellers. The Bible is a "book of books," divided between old and new, poetry, history, dozens of other categories that fill libraries as well as minds and hearts from little children to the aged scholars who rightly divide the text. Of those books, one stands alone as the most widely read, translated, and distributed. Written by the disciple uniquely described as "the beloved," this book is often the first that a new believer is told to read. It is mother's milk to the newly born again and forever loved for the heartfelt and simple cadence that John strikes upon the heart of believers everywhere. "In the beginning was the Word" begins John's recollection, and he ends his story this way, "Jesus did countless things that I haven't included here. And if every one of his works were written down and described one by one, I suppose that the world itself wouldn't have enough room to contain the books that would have to be written!" (John 21:25).

Imparting the gospel and one's very life in daily activities and relationships, vocation and community

> LOVE THE LORD YOUR GOD WITH ALL YOUR HEART, SOUL AND MIND

…and love your neighbor as you love yourself. The whole law and the prophets depend on these two commandments" (Matthew 22:37–40 NASB).

REREAD JOHN 10 EACH DAY REFLECTING ON A DIFFERENT ASPECT OF HIS LOVE.

DAY 1

L3

Experiencing God as He really is through deepened intimacy with Him

I. **Reflect on how the REAL God is a God of love.** How might this text lead me to better love God? "We love because He first loved us" (1 John 4:19 NASB). We can only love the REAL God with all our "heart, soul, mind, and strength."

A. As you read and reflect on the chapter, how might you describe the REAL God as He is seen as Father, Son, and Holy Spirit?

1. In verse_____, He is seen as _____
   _____.

2. In verse _____, He is seen as _____
   _____.

3. In verse _____ , the love of Jesus is seen toward_____
   as He _____.

4. In verse _____ , the love of Jesus is seen toward_____
   as He _____.

5. How might these insights challenge some of your misconceptions of God?

   Sadly, I sometimes mistakenly see God as _____
   _____.

DAY 2

W1

Frequently being led by the Spirit into deeper love for the One who wrote the Word

B. **Reflect on how God has loved *you* since He is the same yesterday, today, and forever (Hebrews 13:8). Pause to let Him love you.**

1. *Father, as you express yourself to me as the God who* _____
   _____, *my heart is moved with*
   _____.

2. *Father, as you express yourself to me as the God who* _____
   _____, *my heart is moved with*
   _____.

C. Jesus is available to love you like we read of His love in this chapter. Pause to express your heart to Him as you see Him in this chapter.

1. Describe how Jesus has loved you in some of the same ways that you read of His love in this chapter:

   I have experienced the love of Jesus as He has _____
   _____.

2. *Jesus, as you love me like you loved those in this chapter, my heart is touched with* _____.

DAY 3

P5

Ministering His life and love to our nearest ones at home and with family as well as faithful engagement in His body, the church

II. **Reflect on how you can better love your "near ones."** How might this text lead me to better love others? "As I have loved you, so you also should love one another." (John 13:34 NASB).

Since we have freely received of His love, we are to freely give this same love to others. Consider again how you see love portrayed in this chapter.

A. Who among your family or friends might you better love?

1. *I could better love_____,*
   especially by _____.

DAY 4

M1

Imparting the gospel and one's very life in daily activities and relationships, vocation and community

B. **Reflect on how you might be a witness of His love.** Notice again how Jesus expressed love by accepting, forgiving, or sacrificing? How might Jesus have taken initiative, expressed compassion, offered support, shared truth, and eternal hope?

1. Who in the traffic patterns of your life might benefit from receiving the blessing of Christ's love through you?
   (Who)_____could benefit from my sharing the love of Jesus by _____.

2. Who in your life could benefit from sharing part of your life story of encountering truth and eternal hope?
   (Who)_____could benefit from my sharing more of
   _____.

3. Pause now to pray for this person and then for yourself as you impart both your life and the gospel.

DAY 5

L4

Rejoicing regularly in my identity as "His Beloved"

III. **Reflect on *you* as the recipient of His love.** Your significance, value, and worth have been established by your Creator through the gift of His Son. How might this text affirm your identity as "His Beloved"?

"The light of God's love shined within us when he sent his matchless Son into the world so that we might live through him." (1 John 4:9).

Celebrate how you have received His love and grace, His forgiveness and new life, His calling and kingdom purpose.

A. Reread the text as His truth being shared just for you.

1. *I'm grateful that I have experienced the blessing of verse _____*
   as I _____.

B. Since He is the same yesterday, today, and forever, meditate on your being *in* the story of this chapter. Allow Him to love you as you read of His love in the chapter.

1. *My heart is touched with gratitude that Jesus _____*
   _____.

Walking in the Light of God's People

"A thief has only one thing in mind—he wants to steal, slaughter, and destroy. But I came to give you everything in abundance, more than you expect—life in its fullness until you overflow!" (John 10:10).

SPIRIT
EMPOWERED
Faith

L2

Listening to and hearing God for direction and discernment

The promised abundant life is His life expressed through us by the Holy Spirit. Abundant life comes through the Christ-like character of Jesus.

Quietly listen before the Lord as His Spirit speaks of needed Christ-like character in your life. Ask the Lord to give you discernment and direction as you respond to the following:

Lord, I sense a needed fresh work of servanthood in me, particularly toward _____.
(which person/persons in your life?)

Holy Spirit, I long for the humility of Christ to be more real in my life through my dependence upon you, my vulnerability before you and others, and my approachability.

Who might benefit from your dependence on the Lord? Your vulnerability? Your approachability?

_____

Lord Jesus, I need a strengthening of your faith in me, that I might believe you for great things. Particularly, I want to trust you for...

_____
_____
_____

Now, stand in faith against the "thief" who seeks to steal and destroy abundance. *"Free me, Holy Spirit, from all of life's anxieties so that my heart might rest secure in you. Help me to cease any attempts to fearfully and selfishly take that which you've promised to supply."*

Lord, forgive me, as there have been times that I have taken your grace for granted. I want your Spirit to stir within me a sensitive and grateful heart. Overwhelm me with a deep awareness of my identity as the beloved of God. Constrain and control me through the grateful wonder of your love.

Now share with your partner or small group at least one of the ways that His Spirit might want to make changes in you. Pray together, with each of you asking God to change you in these ways. Ask Him to deepen your servant's heart and to humble your walk before Him and others. Implore Him to strengthen your faith, casting out all of your anxiety. Ask His Spirit to fill you with the gratitude for His wondrous love.

Walking in the Light of God's Son

Through Fresh Encounters With Jesus   John 12:35; John 8:12

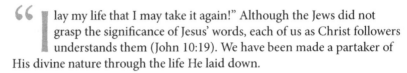

❝ I lay my life that I may take it again!" Although the Jews did not grasp the significance of Jesus' words, each of us as Christ followers understands them (John 10:19). We have been made a partaker of His divine nature through the life He laid down.

"[God] made Him who knew no sin to be sin on our behalf, so that we might become the righteousness of God in Him" (2 Corinthians 5:21 NASB).

Pause and consider Christ's cry to His Father from the cross: "My God, my God, why have you forsaken me?" (Matthew 27:46 NASB). As Jesus took our sin on Himself, the Father, in His holiness, had to turn away. Then Christ through the Holy Spirit would take up His life again!

Reflect once more on being born again. Why did Christ become sin? Even more personally, for whom did He do it? Who will benefit from His resurrection?

Quietly listen to His Spirit whisper the words to your soul: "He did it for you. He did it for you!" The One who knew no sin became sin (2 Corinthians 5:21). If He did not need to die for any other person in the whole world, He would have died for you—and He did die for you!

Allow yourself to respond to this glorious truth. He was raised for you. Meditate on the thought, or even whisper the words, "He did it for me." Is your heart moved with wonder, humility, and joy? Does gratitude and praise fill your soul?

Now share these feelings with God. Give thanks for His initiative in manifesting His glory and presence to you. He laid down His life—and took it up again—for you!

Lord, I am so grateful that _____

_____

_____

_____.

L2

Listening to and hearing God for direction and discernment

Walking in the Light of God's Word

Through Frequent Experience of Scripture   John 12:35; Psalm 119:105

"My own sheep will hear my voice and I know each one, and they will follow me" (John 10:27).

Listening to and hearing God for direction and discernment

Hearing Jesus is critical to following Him. His voice is not unclear or uncertain but often it's our hearing that is impaired. To follow Him faithfully requires freedom to hear.

Be still before the Lord and offer the same prayer that David prayed as you seek to put away things that might hinder you from hearing God.

"Search me, O God, and know my heart; Try me and know my anxious thoughts…see if there be any hurtful way in me and lead me in the everlasting way" (Psalm 139:23–24 NASB).

- Search me, O Lord, for sins that hinder me from hearing You. Free me from all moral filth, evil, malice, deceit, hypocrisy, envy, and slander. Free me to have a cleansed heart and mind. Speak now, your servant listens. *I need to put away…*

- Search me, O Lord, for unresolved emotions that keep me from hearing you. Free me from any guilt or condemnation, any anger or bitterness, any fear or anxiety. Free me to live each moment "in the present" with you. Speak now your servant listens. *I need to put away…*

- Search me, O Lord, for childish things that distract me from hearing you. Free me from rationalizing my behavior and blaming others, from idle chatter and self-focus. Free me to practice personal responsibility before you and others. Speak now, your servant listens. *I need to put away…*

- Self-initiative prevents me from hearing you. Free me from my thoughts, my ways, my ideas, and my goals. May I instead embrace your thoughts, yours ways, your ideas, and your goals. Speak now, your servant listens. *I need to put away…*

Pause and wait before the Lord. Listen as He reveals what needs to be put away. Now yield to Him, even though you may not fully know all that will be necessary:

Lord I sense the need to put away _____

_____ *from my life.*

Even before fully knowing all that may be required. I yield to you. I long to hear you. Remove this from my life so that I can more freely hear what you reveal to me. In Jesus' name, amen."

SPIRIT
EMPOWERED
Faith

L2

Listening to and hearing
God for direction and
discernment

> **LOVE THE LORD YOUR GOD WITH ALL YOUR HEART, SOUL AND MIND**
>
> …and love your neighbor as you love yourself. The whole law and the prophets depend on these two commandments" (Matthew 22:37–40 NASB).

REREAD JOHN 11 EACH DAY REFLECTING ON A DIFFERENT ASPECT OF HIS LOVE.

DAY 1

L3

Experiencing God as He really is through deepened intimacy with Him

I. **Reflect on how the REAL God is a God of love.** How might this text lead me to better love God? "We love because He first loved us" (1 John 4:19 NASB). We can only love the REAL God with all our "heart, soul, mind, and strength."

A. As you read and reflect on the chapter, how might you describe the REAL God as He is seen as Father, Son, and Holy Spirit?

1. In verse_____, He is seen as _____.

2. In verse _____, He is seen as _____.

3. In verse _____, the love of Jesus is seen toward_____ as He _____.

4. In verse _____, the love of Jesus is seen toward_____ as He _____.

5. How might these insights challenge some of your misconceptions of God?

   Sadly, I sometimes mistakenly see God as _____ _____.

DAY 2

W1

Frequently being led by the Spirit into deeper love for the One who wrote the Word

B. **Reflect on how God has loved *you*** since He is the same yesterday, today, and forever (Hebrews 13:8). **Pause to let Him love you.**

1. *Father, as you express yourself to me as the God who* _____ _____, *my heart is moved with* _____.

2. *Father, as you express yourself to me as the God who* _____ _____, *my heart is moved with* _____.

C. Jesus is available to love you like we read of His love in this chapter. Pause to express your heart to Him as you see Him in this chapter.

1. Describe how Jesus has loved you in some of the same ways that you read of His love in this chapter:

   I have experienced the love of Jesus as He has _____ _____.

2. *Jesus, as you love me like you loved those in this chapter, my heart is touched with* _____.

DAY 3

P5

Ministering His life and love to our nearest ones at home and with family as well as faithful engagement in His body, the church

II. **Reflect on how you can better love your "near ones."** How might this text lead me to better love others? "As I have loved you, so you also should love one another." (John 13:34 NASB).

Since we have freely received of His love, we are to freely give this same love to others. Consider again how you see love portrayed in this chapter.

A. Who among your family or friends might you better love?

1. *I could better love_____,*
   especially by _____.

DAY 4

M1

Imparting the gospel and one's very life in daily activities and relationships, vocation and community

B. **Reflect on how you might be a witness of His love.** Notice again how Jesus expressed love by accepting, forgiving, or sacrificing? How might Jesus have taken initiative, expressed compassion, offered support, shared truth, and eternal hope?

1. Who in the traffic patterns of your life might benefit from receiving the blessing of Christ's love through you?
   (Who)_____could benefit from my sharing the love of Jesus by _____.

2. Who in your life could benefit from sharing part of your life story of encountering truth and eternal hope?
   (Who)_____could benefit from my sharing more of
   _____.

3. Pause now to pray for this person and then for yourself as you impart both your life and the gospel.

DAY 5

L4

Rejoicing regularly in my identity as "His Beloved"

III. **Reflect on *you* as the recipient of His love.** Your significance, value, and worth have been established by your Creator through the gift of His Son. How might this text affirm your identity as "His Beloved"?

"The light of God's love shined within us when he sent his matchless Son into the world so that we might live through him." (1 John 4:9).

Celebrate how you have received His love and grace, His forgiveness and new life, His calling and kingdom purpose.

A. Reread the text as His truth being shared just for you.

1. *I'm grateful that I have experienced the blessing of verse _____*
   as I _____.

B. Since He is the same yesterday, today, and forever, meditate on your being *in* the story of this chapter. Allow Him to love you as you read of His love in the chapter.

1. *My heart is touched with gratitude that Jesus _____*
   _____.

Walking in the Light of God's People

"Jesus loved Miriam, Martha, and Lazarus" (John 11:5).

It's important to remember that Jesus fulfilled all that His Father intended for Him as a single person. Scripture records that as He entered His teen years, He "increased in wisdom and stature, and in favor with God and men" (Luke 2:52). Notice His mental and physical growth, as well as His spiritual. Also important is that Jesus developed "favor" with others. He was a good student, worker, son, brother, and a good friend!

"In the village of Bethany there was a man named Lazarus, and his sisters, Miriam and Martha" (John 11:1). During His public ministry, the Gospels mention that Jesus makes several trips to Bethany, a small village outside of Jerusalem (see Luke 10:38–42). There seems to be no apparent religious or political significance to the village, and yet it is important to Jesus because His three friends live there!

Miriam, Martha, and Lazarus appear to be sources of fellowship for Jesus. As good friends, Jesus is welcomed into their home, meals are taken together, times of significant conversation occur, tears are shed together, and others notice the love of four friends.

P3

Discerning the relational needs of others with a heart to give His love

Startling people with loving initiatives can lead to meaningful fellowship.

People are lovable because they are created by the One who is love. "Jesus loved Miriam, Martha, and Lazarus" (John 11:5). Jesus validates others' lovableness by giving first to them.

God provides people for us to love through meaningful fellowship. "Look how much he loved Lazarus" (John 11:36). Others observe Jesus' love for His friends and are startled.

God provides people to love us through meaningful fellowship. "Miriam was the one who would anoint Jesus' feet with costly perfume and dry his feet with her long hair" (John 11:2). Jesus receives love from others who care deeply for Him.

Pause to list people in your life who serve as sources of fellowship…

- Given that people are worthy of love, to whom might you say, "You are lovable"?
- Express gratitude to God for the people with whom you have enjoyed hospitality, had meals together, shared significant conversation, shed tears, and cared for so deeply that others noticed your closeness.
- To whom might you take initiative to "give first" by showing appreciation, providing encouragement, giving comfort, offering support.

Lord, thanks for blessing my friendships, especially with _____.

Just as Jesus would express care and concern for these three that He loved in Bethany (John 11:5), how might God want to additionally express love to friends in your life? Pray now with your partner or small group and ask Him: *Dear Lord, show me not only who to love but also how to love him/her in relevant ways.*

Walking in the Light of God's Word

Through Frequent Experience of Scripture   John 12:35; Psalm 119:105

"He remained where he was for two more days" (John 11:6).

Jesus heard the Word of His Father and courageously yielded to it. In John 11, we observe an example of the Father revealing His Word and the Son exhibiting courage to yield to His Father's will, despite a request from His friends.

"One day Lazarus became very sick to the point of death. So his sisters sent a message to Jesus, 'Lord, our brother Lazarus, the one you love, is very sick. Please come!'" (John 11:23).

Listening to and hearing God's Word...

- **Informs judgment.** "He remained where he was for two more days" (John 11:6).

- **Empowers courage.** "Finally, on the third day, he said to his disciples, 'Come. It's time to go to Bethany'" (John 11:7).

- **Clarifies vision.** "This sickness will not end in death for Lazarus, but will bring glory and praise to God. This will reveal the greatness of the Son of God by what takes place" (John 11:4).

SPIRIT EMPOWERED *Faith*

P3

Discerning the relational needs of others with a heart to give His love

Pause and practice allowing God's Spirit to make the written Word the living Word.

Ask God to reveal through His Word the areas in your life in which your opinions might be coloring your judgment:

Lord, help my beliefs, behaviors, and relational encounters to be in alignment with your Word.

Ask the Lord to empower your decision making:

Heavenly Father, may I have the boldness to address issues in my own life and to offer courageous confessions when appropriate. Help me to stand for what is right and not "cave in" to others' pressure. Also, Father, grant the awareness and the grace to hold others accountable for their growth!

Ask God to provide clarity and confirmation through His Word regarding His will in your current situation:

Lord, give me a clear purpose in life and the ability to support and encourage others in following a clear purpose.

Walking in the Light of God's Son

Through Fresh Encounters With Jesus   John 12:35; John 8:12

"Jesus comforted people throughout His time on earth, sometimes identifying with others' pain to the point of weeping for them" (John 11:35).

P3

Discerning the relational needs of others with a heart to give His love

Jesus comforted people throughout His time on earth, sometimes identifying with others' pain to the point of weeping for them (John 11:35; Luke 19:41). Even on the eve of His own death, He comforted the disciples because He sensed their sorrow and anxiety (John 14:1, 18, 27; 16:3).

We are impressed by two miracles in this chapter: the raising of Lazarus from the dead and the miracle of a God who cries! Imagine "weep with those who weep" (Romans 12:15) and think that there is a "blessing" available when we mourn. The blessing is called comfort (Matthew 5:4).

Jesus was moved deeply within His spirit as He wept with His friend Miriam. Comfort flowed through the prompting and power of the Comforter. For us, comfort may be as simple as sharing "I'm really sorry that happened." Very often the Holy Spirit's first work is to take captive and resist our common, unhelpful, or unproductive responses.

Consider that Jesus could have but *didn't* give these unhelpful responses:

- **Advice/instruction:** "Let me tell you how to solve the problem." "Maybe next time that happens you should . . ."
- **Logic/reasoning:** "Let me analyze the situation and tell you why it happened." "I think that happened because . . ."
- **Pep talk:** "You're a winner! You'll make it through these tough times!" "I'm sure tomorrow will be a better day."
- **Minimize the incident:** "Sure it hurt, but there's still a lot going on that's good." "Aren't you being overly sensitive?"
- **Spiritualizing:** "Well, you know that God will work all this out for your good." "Joseph's brothers meant evil for him, but God meant it for good." "It's good to know that we are more than conquerors through Christ!"

Each response seems to work best after we give comfort.

Jesus has compassion for us. "When Jesus looked at Miriam and saw her weeping at his feet, and all her friends who were with her grieving, he was deeply moved with tenderness and compassion...Then tears streamed down Jesus' face" (John 11:33, 35). Jesus not only hurts for people named Miriam in Bethany, but He also hurts for us. We can approach Jesus with our pain, knowing that He cares for us.

Pause and experience Jesus' comfort...

- Recall a painful life event, remembering how you felt (e.g., disappointed, rejected, alone). Now imagine Jesus comes near to you, gently calling your name. As you turn, you see Jesus' tender eyes filled with compassionate tears for you.
- Thank Jesus for caring so much: *"Dear Jesus, I'm grateful that you cared enough to come looking for me. Thank you for your compassionate, caring heart toward my pain."*

My Journal

P3

Discerning the relational needs of others with a heart to give His love

> LOVE THE LORD YOUR GOD WITH ALL YOUR HEART, SOUL AND MIND
>
> ...and love your neighbor as you love yourself. The whole law and the prophets depend on these two commandments" (Matthew 22:37–40 NASB).

REREAD JOHN 12 EACH DAY REFLECTING ON A DIFFERENT ASPECT OF HIS LOVE.

DAY 1

SPIRIT EMPOWERED
Faith

L3

Experiencing God as He really is through deepened intimacy with Him

I. **Reflect on how the REAL God is a God of love.** How might this text lead me to better love God? "We love because He first loved us" (1 John 4:19 NASB). We can only love the REAL God with all our "heart, soul, mind, and strength."

A. As you read and reflect on the chapter, how might you describe the REAL God as He is seen as Father, Son, and Holy Spirit?

1. In verse_____, He is seen as _____
_____.

2. In verse _____, He is seen as _____
_____.

3. In verse _____, the love of Jesus is seen toward_____
as He _____.

4. In verse _____, the love of Jesus is seen toward_____
as He _____.

5. How might these insights challenge some of your misconceptions of God?

Sadly, I sometimes mistakenly see God as _____
_____.

DAY 2

SPIRIT EMPOWERED
Faith

W1

Frequently being led by the Spirit into deeper love for the One who wrote the Word

B. **Reflect on how God has loved *you*** since He is the same yesterday, today, and forever (Hebrews 13:8). **Pause to let Him love you.**

1. *Father, as you express yourself to me as the God who* _____
_____, *my heart is moved with*
_____.

2. *Father, as you express yourself to me as the God who* _____
_____, *my heart is moved with*
_____.

C. Jesus is available to love you like we read of His love in this chapter. Pause to express your heart to Him as you see Him in this chapter.

1. Describe how Jesus has loved you in some of the same ways that you read of His love in this chapter:

I have experienced the love of Jesus as He has _____
_____.

2. *Jesus, as you love me like you loved those in this chapter, my heart is touched with* _____.

DAY 3

P5

Ministering His life and love to our nearest ones at home and with family as well as faithful engagement in His body, the church

II. **Reflect on how you can better love your "near ones."** How might this text lead me to better love others? "As I have loved you, so you also should love one another." (John 13:34 NASB).

Since we have freely received of His love, we are to freely give this same love to others. Consider again how you see love portrayed in this chapter.

A. Who among your family or friends might you better love?

1. *I could better love_____,*
   especially by _____.

DAY 4

M1

Imparting the gospel and one's very life in daily activities and relationships, vocation and community

B. **Reflect on how you might be a witness of His love.** Notice again how Jesus expressed love by accepting, forgiving, or sacrificing? How might Jesus have taken initiative, expressed compassion, offered support, shared truth, and eternal hope?

1. Who in the traffic patterns of your life might benefit from receiving the blessing of Christ's love through you?
   (Who)_____could benefit from my sharing the love of Jesus by _____.

2. Who in your life could benefit from sharing part of your life story of encountering truth and eternal hope?
   (Who)_____could benefit from my sharing more of
   _____

3. Pause now to pray for this person and then for yourself as you impart both your life and the gospel.

DAY 5

L4

Rejoicing regularly in my identity as "His Beloved"

III. **Reflect on *you* as the recipient of His love.** Your significance, value, and worth have been established by your Creator through the gift of His Son. How might this text affirm your identity as "His Beloved"?

"The light of God's love shined within us when he sent his matchless Son into the world so that we might live through him." (1 John 4:9).

Celebrate how you have received His love and grace, His forgiveness and new life, His calling and kingdom purpose.

A. Reread the text as His truth being shared just for you.

1. *I'm grateful that I have experienced the blessing of verse _____*
   as I _____.

B. Since He is the same yesterday, today, and forever, meditate on your being *in* the story of this chapter. Allow Him to love you as you read of His love in the chapter.

1. *My heart is touched with gratitude that Jesus _____*
   _____

Walking in the Light of God's People

Through Faithful Engagement in Fellowship   John 12:35; Matthew 5:14

"Six days before the Passover began, Jesus went back to Bethany, the town where he raised Lazarus from the dead. They had prepared a supper for Jesus" (John 12:1–2).

SPIRIT EMPOWERED *Faith*

W3

Yielding to the Scripture's protective cautions and transforming power to bring life change in me

I n John 12:1–8, Jesus validates that we are created to relate. "Six days before the Passover began, Jesus went back to Bethany, the town where he raised Lazarus from the dead" (John 12:1). He returns to Bethany to connect with His friends.

Relating to others involves…

- **Prioritizing people over projects.** Jesus puts people first. He has a mission to fulfill, and yet he made connecting with others a priority.

- **Being served by others.** "They had prepared a supper for Jesus. Martha served…Miriam anointed Jesus' feet. Then she wiped them dry with her long hair. And the fragrance of the costly oil filled the house" (John 12:2–3). Although Jesus comes to serve, He also takes time to receive.

- **Courageously addressing concerns with others.** "Jesus said to Judas, 'Leave her alone! She has saved it for the time of my burial. You'll always have the poor with you; but you won't always have me'" (John 12:7–8). Jesus boldly confronts Judas' statement: "What a waste! We could have sold this perfume for a fortune and given the money to the poor!" (John 12:5).

Pause to explore with a partner or group member how you might be…

- Neglecting important relationships in your life. Answer the following questions: How might I put people first in my life? Who could benefit from receiving from me? How might I give first to this person?

- Too proud to receive from others. Pray with your group members about having more humility to be served by others. Others have feedback to offer you. God would want to involve others in meeting some of your relational needs.

- Avoiding a problem that needs to be addressed. Ask your group members to hold you accountable to confront difficult people in your life. Perhaps offer a confession about how you might have contributed to the relational disconnect.

Now pray together, asking that the Holy Spirit make you a great "friend" to those in your life:

Dear Holy Spirit, help me to cherish the important people in my life, giving care to them and receiving from them as well.

Walking in the Light of God's Son

Through Fresh Encounters With Jesus   John 12:35; John 8:12

"Then suddenly a booming voice was heard from the sky, 'I have glorified my name! And I will glorify it through you again!'" (John 12:28).

L7

Entering often into Spirit-led praise and worship

Entering often into Spirit-led praise and worship seems to be characterized by…

- **Celebrating with praises** (*eulageo*). "Everyone was shouting, 'Lord, be our Savior! Blessed is the one who comes to us sent from Jehovah-God, the King of Israel'" (John 12:13).

- **Casting out fear.** "Then Jesus found a young donkey and rode on it to fulfill what was prophesied: 'People of Zion, have no fear!'" (John 12:14).

- **Exalting Jesus.** "All the eyewitnesses kept spreading the news about Jesus to everyone…Isaiah said these things because he had seen and experienced the splendor of Jesus and prophesied about him" (John 12:17, 41).

- **Drawing others to Him.** "Now there were a number of foreigners from among the nations who were worshipers at the feast. They went to Philip…and they asked him, 'Would you take us to see Jesus?'" (John 12:20–21).

- **Practicing selflessness.** "A single grain of wheat will never be more than a single grain of wheat unless it drops into the ground and dies…For I have come to fulfill my purpose—to offer myself to God" (John 12:24, 27).

- **Growing faith.** "Then Jesus told them, 'The voice you heard was not for my benefit, but for yours—to help you believe'" (John 12:30).

- **Awakening spiritually.** "[T]he ruler of this dark world will be overthrown…I have come as a light to shine in this dark world so that all who trust in me will no longer wander in darkness" (John 12:31, 46).

Share with Jesus your hope regarding worship:

Lord, I'm hoping my worship of you will be characterized more by

_____

_____

and less by _____

_____.

Walking in the Light of God's Word

Through Frequent Experience of Scripture   John 12:35; Psalm 119:105

"...walk in the light..." (John 12:35).

Each of us has known of family or friends who started out following Jesus, only to be overtaken by the darkness of sin, self, or Satan. How do we understand such return to worldliness, cold-heartedness, and rebellion?

In John 12:35–36, 46, Christ shares this illustration: the darkness is always chasing us, and all we have to do for it to overtake us is to stop walking in God's light! So how are we to understand God's light, and how are we to walk in it?

To walk in His light involves frequent and recurring encounters with…

- **Jesus**—"Then Jesus spoke to them again, saying, 'I am the light of the world. He who follows Me shall not walk in darkness, but have the light of life'" (John 8:12). We can practice the presence of the Lord, yielding to the Spirit's work of Christ-likeness.

- **Scripture**—"Your word is a lamp to my feet and a light to my path" (Psalm 119:105 NASB). We can life "naturally supernatural" in all of life as God's Spirit makes the written Word (*logos*) the living Word (*Rhema*).

- **Followers of Jesus**—"You are the light of the world" (Matthew 5:14 NASB). We can take courageous initiative as a peacemaker, reconciling relationships along life's journey.

The Holy Spirit within us is also critical to our walking in God's light. It is the Holy Spirit that reveals Jesus to us (see John 14:26); brings illumination to Scripture (see 1 John 2:27), and empowers our fellowship together as Christ's followers (see 1 Corinthians 12:2–13). How's your walk?

W3

Yielding to the Scripture's protective cautions and transforming power to bring life change in me

With your group members discuss the three sources of light—God's Son, His Scripture, and His Saints.

- **Celebrate together one of the areas in which you are thriving:**

  I'm doing well at yielding to Scripture's protective cautions and transforming work through the Word.

- **Pray together about one of the areas in which you could benefit from more exercise in walking in the light:**

  Lord, help me to experience you as you really are through deepened intimacy with you!

My Journal

JOHN BEGINS AT THE HEIGHTS OF CREATION and ends with the thrill of more to come. Oh the stories that were told and the ones yet to be told in heaven! Between those two grand thoughts is the love letter written to saints and prodigals alike from the Father of lights, lived by the Savior Son, and inspired by the Creator Spirit of holiness.

SPIRIT
EMPOWERED
Faith
W3

Yielding to the Scripture's protective cautions and transforming power to bring life change in me

> LOVE THE LORD YOUR GOD WITH ALL YOUR HEART, SOUL AND MIND
>
> …and love your neighbor as you love yourself. The whole law and the prophets depend on these two commandments" (Matthew 22:37–40 NASB).

REREAD JOHN 13 EACH DAY REFLECTING ON A DIFFERENT ASPECT OF HIS LOVE.

DAY 1

L3

Experiencing God as He really is through deepened intimacy with Him

I. **Reflect on how the REAL God is a God of love.** How might this text lead me to better love God? "We love because He first loved us" (1 John 4:19 NASB). We can only love the REAL God with all our "heart, soul, mind, and strength."

A. As you read and reflect on the chapter, how might you describe the REAL God as He is seen as Father, Son, and Holy Spirit?

1. In verse_____, He is seen as _____
    _____.

2. In verse _____, He is seen as _____
    _____.

3. In verse _____, the love of Jesus is seen toward_____
    as He _____.

4. In verse _____, the love of Jesus is seen toward_____
    as He _____.

5. How might these insights challenge some of your misconceptions of God?

    Sadly, I sometimes mistakenly see God as _____
    _____.

DAY 2

W1

Frequently being led by the Spirit into deeper love for the One who wrote the Word

B. **Reflect on how God has loved *you*** since He is the same yesterday, today, and forever (Hebrews 13:8). **Pause to let Him love you.**

1. *Father, as you express yourself to me as the God who* _____
    _____, *my heart is moved with*
    _____.

2. *Father, as you express yourself to me as the God who* _____
    _____, *my heart is moved with*
    _____.

C. Jesus is available to love you like we read of His love in this chapter. Pause to express your heart to Him as you see Him in this chapter.

1. Describe how Jesus has loved you in some of the same ways that you read of His love in this chapter:

    I have experienced the love of Jesus as He has _____
    _____.

2. *Jesus, as you love me like you loved those in this chapter, my heart is touched with* _____.

DAY 3

P5

Ministering His life and love to our nearest ones at home and with family as well as faithful engagement in His body, the church

II. **Reflect on how you can better love your "near ones."** How might this text lead me to better love others? "As I have loved you, so you also should love one another." (John 13:34 NASB).

Since we have freely received of His love, we are to freely give this same love to others. Consider again how you see love portrayed in this chapter.

A. Who among your family or friends might you better love?

1. *I could better love_____,*
   especially by _____.

DAY 4

M1

Imparting the gospel and one's very life in daily activities and relationships, vocation and community

B. **Reflect on how you might be a witness of His love.** Notice again how Jesus expressed love by accepting, forgiving, or sacrificing? How might Jesus have taken initiative, expressed compassion, offered support, shared truth, and eternal hope?

1. Who in the traffic patterns of your life might benefit from receiving the blessing of Christ's love through you?
   (Who)_____could benefit from my sharing the love of Jesus by _____.

2. Who in your life could benefit from sharing part of your life story of encountering truth and eternal hope?
   (Who)_____could benefit from my sharing more of
   _____.

3. Pause now to pray for this person and then for yourself as you impart both your life and the gospel.

DAY 5

L4

Rejoicing regularly in my identity as "His Beloved"

III. **Reflect on *you* as the recipient of His love.** Your significance, value, and worth have been established by your Creator through the gift of His Son. How might this text affirm your identity as "His Beloved"?

"The light of God's love shined within us when he sent his matchless Son into the world so that we might live through him." (1 John 4:9).

Celebrate how you have received His love and grace, His forgiveness and new life, His calling and kingdom purpose.

A. Reread the text as His truth being shared just for you.

1. *I'm grateful that I have experienced the blessing of verse _____*
   as I _____.

B. Since He is the same yesterday, today, and forever, meditate on your being *in* the story of this chapter. Allow Him to love you as you read of His love in the chapter.

1. *My heart is touched with gratitude that Jesus _____*
   _____.

Walking in the Light of God's Word

Through Frequent Experience of Scripture   John 12:35; Psalm 119:105

"Now Jesus was fully aware that the Father had placed all things under his control, for he had come from God and was about to go back to be with him" (John 13:3).

Championing Jesus as the only hope of eternal life and abundant living

Is this any less true today? Is Jesus any less aware? Is He any less in control? Is he not interceding for you before the Father right now?

"He always lives to make intercession for them" (Hebrews 7:25 NASB).

The ministry of Jesus is complete and absolute. His life spent on earth proved the character and forged the Redeemer's everlasting ministry as the One who now lives to bring our petitions, prayers, and praise before the Father's throne. It's true. He really does hold the whole world in His hand.

Imagine heaven! The very atmosphere a sweet aroma of praise that raises like the cloud that Isaiah saw in his vision. In the throne room of heaven, stands one who looks like the Son of God! Beseeching. His voice rising and falling with faith, hope, and love for His church. From the mouth of the One risen from the dead, your name is spoken. You—Jesus is interceding for you.

Paul said in Philippians 4:6 to "make your request known to God."

Is there a wayward child your heart breaks for? Is there a soul that you cry out for? Is there a purpose in life you are asking for? See the Lord, high and lifted up, His scarred hands spread before the Father, and His voice filling the celestial air with faith. He carries your petitions before the throne.

It is time to pray with new faith, friend. Let your request go to the One who intercedes before the Father.

- Make your request known, *"Jesus, I bring my need, petition, prayer, and request before you now."*

- Begin to thank Him as He takes your petition and presents it before the throne.

- Close your eyes and imagine the scene in heaven as your Lord delivers your petition before Father God.

There is only one response adequate, and that is praise to the One who lives to make intercession for you. Let His kingdom come here on this earth just like it is in heaven.

Walking in the Light of God's Son

Through Fresh Encounters With Jesus   John 12:35; John 8:12

"You've called me your teacher and lord, and you're right, for that's who I am. So if I'm your teacher and lord and have just washed your dirty feet, then you should follow the example that I've set for you and wash one another's dirty feet. Now do for each other what I have just done for you" (John 13:13–15).

Championing Jesus as the only hope of eternal life and abundant living

"**O**ne and done." That is the phrase people use when something is done once and never repeated. It's over and done with, complete, move on…nothing to see here.

Yet, the good news is that Jesus is still washing feet. He is still the great and mighty Lord of all who washes the feet—and hearts, and souls—of whosoever will come (Mark 8:34). Right now, you have a divine appointment with the scarred hands of the Messiah. In His kingdom, He rules by serving.

I know. It is hard to come—a bit embarrassing to keep dragging mud behind you. Come anyway. His ministry, His greatest joy, will not be completed until you see Him face to face. Maturity is the distance between sin and repentance. The shorter the distance, the greater the maturity. Waste no time. He stands ready to serve.

Pray like this: *Lord, I know I am in great need of your cleansing grace right now. Look at me, Lord…I'm a mess. Thank you that you never refuse repentance. You never refuse those who come in humility. I confess (name the sin and failure) and ask you to cleanse me. Thank you, Lord, that you continue to wash dirty feet!*

The task is not complete though with repentance. Jesus said, "You also ought to wash another's feet." Who do you know that needs the tender compassion and acceptance that Jesus has shown you? Muddy feet are usually left to others to care for, but not today. Today the Lord appoints you to be His hands and His heart.

So go and do the same! **Ask Him now:**

Holy Spirit, who would you send me to that I might champion Jesus as our only hope of life and life abundant?

Walking in the Light of God's People
Through Faithful Engagement in Fellowship   John 12:35; Matthew 5:14

"So I give you now a new commandment: Love each other just as much as I have loved you. For when you demonstrate the same love I have for you by loving one another, everyone will know that you're my true followers" (John 13:34–35).

Championing Jesus as the only hope of eternal life and abundant living

With these words, Jesus is both reminding the disciples of His past demonstrations of love and concern for them as well as foreshadowing His forthcoming display of perfect love at Calvary. Through His sacrifice, and through His continual caring involvement in our lives, Jesus has loved us as well. The more we recognize and receive His love; the more we are able to embrace our true identity as His beloved.

Consider what Scripture reveals about God's love for us:

- God demonstrated His love for us by sending Jesus to die for us while we were still sinners (Romans 5:8).

- Nothing can separate us from God's love (Romans 8:38–39).

- He has poured out His love upon us through the Holy Spirit (Romans 5:5).

- The love of Christ for us is infinitely great and surpasses knowledge (Ephesians 3:18–19).

- Because of His great love for us, God made us alive with Christ (Ephesians 2:4–5).

We are not simply people who believe Scripture's great doctrines about Christ, nor are we merely people who practice good behavior. Hopefully, we do believe right doctrine and practice right behavior, but we must be careful not to think that our identity lies in either of these things. Our true identity is that we are ones who have been loved by Jesus. We are His beloved.

Jesus left behind exact instructions with the disciples as to how the world was to know about Him. His intent was that the love that the disciples declared they had for Him would be demonstrated in practical and observable love for one another. In other words, the world would believe in the love of God because His people truly loved one another.

One of the best ways to show the love of God to one another is through affirmation. Affirmation is the recognition in another's life of God's grace. When we affirm one another, we are validating the work of the Holy Spirit in someone.

- *I've noticed how patient you have been lately, and I see how God has worked in your life.*

- *I've really seen God's love in you recently, especially in the way you treat your kids.*

- *I know times have been tough, but I have witnessed how graciously you've walked through the heartache you've experienced.*

This is not a pep talk but recognition of what God has done by affirming with words that validate.

Championing Jesus as the only hope of eternal life and abundant living

> **LOVE THE LORD YOUR GOD WITH ALL YOUR HEART, SOUL AND MIND**
>
> …and love your neighbor as you love yourself. The whole law and the prophets depend on these two commandments" (Matthew 22:37–40 NASB).

REREAD JOHN 14 EACH DAY REFLECTING ON A DIFFERENT ASPECT OF HIS LOVE.

DAY 1

L3

Experiencing God as He really is through deepened intimacy with Him

I. **Reflect on how the REAL God is a God of love.** How might this text lead me to better love God? "We love because He first loved us" (1 John 4:19 NASB). We can only love the REAL God with all our "heart, soul, mind, and strength."

A. As you read and reflect on the chapter, how might you describe the REAL God as He is seen as Father, Son, and Holy Spirit?

1. In verse_____, He is seen as _____
_____.

2. In verse _____, He is seen as _____
_____.

3. In verse _____, the love of Jesus is seen toward_____
as He _____.

4. In verse _____, the love of Jesus is seen toward_____
as He _____.

5. How might these insights challenge some of your misconceptions of God?

   Sadly, I sometimes mistakenly see God as _____
   _____.

DAY 2

W1

Frequently being led by the Spirit into deeper love for the One who wrote the Word

B. **Reflect on how God has loved** *you* since He is the same yesterday, today, and forever (Hebrews 13:8). **Pause to let Him love you.**

1. *Father, as you express yourself to me as the God who* _____
   _____, *my heart is moved with*
   _____.

2. *Father, as you express yourself to me as the God who* _____
   _____, *my heart is moved with*
   _____.

C. Jesus is available to love you like we read of His love in this chapter. Pause to express your heart to Him as you see Him in this chapter.

1. Describe how Jesus has loved you in some of the same ways that you read of His love in this chapter:

   I have experienced the love of Jesus as He has _____
   _____.

2. *Jesus, as you love me like you loved those in this chapter, my heart is touched with* _____.

DAY 3

P5

Ministering His life and love to our nearest ones at home and with family as well as faithful engagement in His body, the church

II. Reflect on how you can better love your "near ones." How might this text lead me to better love others? "As I have loved you, so you also should love one another." (John 13:34 NASB).

Since we have freely received of His love, we are to freely give this same love to others. Consider again how you see love portrayed in this chapter.

A. Who among your family or friends might you better love?

1. *I could better love_____,*
   especially by _____.

DAY 4

M1

Imparting the gospel and one's very life in daily activities and relationships, vocation and community

B. Reflect on how you might be a witness of His love. Notice again how Jesus expressed love by accepting, forgiving, or sacrificing? How might Jesus have taken initiative, expressed compassion, offered support, shared truth, and eternal hope?

1. Who in the traffic patterns of your life might benefit from receiving the blessing of Christ's love through you?
   (Who)_____could benefit from my sharing the love
   of Jesus by _____.

2. Who in your life could benefit from sharing part of your life story of encountering truth and eternal hope?
   (Who)_____could benefit from my sharing more of
   _____.

3. Pause now to pray for this person and then for yourself as you impart both your life and the gospel.

DAY 5

L4

Rejoicing regularly in my identity as "His Beloved"

III. Reflect on *you* as the recipient of His love. Your significance, value, and worth have been established by your Creator through the gift of His Son. How might this text affirm your identity as "His Beloved"?

"The light of God's love shined within us when he sent his matchless Son into the world so that we might live through him." (1 John 4:9).

Celebrate how you have received His love and grace, His forgiveness and new life, His calling and kingdom purpose.

A. Reread the text as His truth being shared just for you.

1. *I'm grateful that I have experienced the blessing of verse _____*
   as I _____.

B. Since He is the same yesterday, today, and forever, meditate on your being *in* the story of this chapter. Allow Him to love you as you read of His love in the chapter.

1. *My heart is touched with gratitude that Jesus _____*
   _____.

Walking in the Light of God's Son

Through Fresh Encounters With Jesus   John 12:35; John 8:12

"Jesus replied, 'Philip, I've been with you all this time and you still don't know who I am? How could you ask me to show you the Father, for anyone who has looked at me has seen the Father?'" (John 14:9).

L3

Experiencing God as He really is through deepened intimacy with Him

Imagine the sadness that must have been in the Savior's heart as He uttered these words. Picture the scene in the upper room. Jesus' faithful followers surround Him. Christ has already experienced the painful distraction of the disciples' argument about who was to be the greatest in the kingdom. He has vulnerably shared how His body is about to be broken and His blood is about to be shed, only to be met with the dispute of His closest friends (Luke 22:17–26).

Then, as a testimony of humble servanthood, Christ takes a basin of water and a towel and begins to wash the feet of each disciple. He washes the feet of Peter, James, John, and even Judas (John 13:5–15). He washes the feet of His betrayer, extending love and grace to him one final time. During the Passover meal, Christ turns to Judas and says, "What you do, do quickly" (John 13:27). Judas then departs to complete the terms of his agreement to betray Christ.

As you revisit this familiar story, pause and reflect upon the heart of the Savior:

- What might Jesus have been feeling as He experienced the dread of crucifixion, the insensitivity of His disciples' response and the anticipation of His imminent betrayal, and the departure of His closest friends?

- What feelings might have been in Christ's heart in the upper room?

- Imagine that this One, who is "a man of sorrows and acquainted with grief", experiences additional pain as He utters His next words (Isaiah 53:3).

- Allow the Holy Spirit to gently lead you to respond to the heart of Jesus as you hear Him say, *"Have I been with you so long, and yet you have not known Me?"*

- Now allow your compassion to prompt your deepened longing to know Him: *"Lord Jesus, I want to better know you. I want to know you for who you really are."* A life of abundance requires fresh, frequent encounters with Jesus to empower and motivate our participation with Him in kingdom living.

Pray like this: *Jesus, as I sense your sadness that your followers have often missed knowing you, my heart is* _____
_____.

As I seek to live a life of revival and blessing, prompt me often Holy Spirit to consistently pursue a deeper knowing of Jesus.

Walking in the Light of God's Word

Through Frequent Experience of Scripture   John 12:35; Psalm 119:105

"Believe that I live as one with my Father and that my Father lives as one with me—or at least, believe because of the mighty miracles I have done" (John 14:11).

SPIRIT EMPOWERED Faith

L3

Experiencing God as He really is through deepened intimacy with Him

When Jesus invited His disciples to "believe Me for the sake of the works themselves" (John 14:11), He referred not only to the evidences that make believing a rational, reasonable exercise but also to the context of the invitation. He invites us to believe in a person. Believing in Christ and His Word will have a profound and relational meaning in each of our lives.

People can have convictions in misguided and wrong beliefs as the terrorist attacks of September 11 prove. We must move beyond subjective believing to a conviction in what is objectively true. Those beliefs must be shown to be not only true but also relevant—that is, relationally meaningful to life.

Having convictions, then, can be defined as "being so thoroughly convinced that Christ and His Word are both objectively true and relationally meaningful that you act on your beliefs regardless of the consequences."

The expression "WWJD" (What Would Jesus Do) likely had its origin in this idea that to live with God-honoring convictions is to live and love as Jesus would. What's He been doing through you lately?

A life of abundance is expressed through the discipline of experiencing Scripture as the Word provides direction and adequacy to answer the question WWJD. God's living Word is the "lamp for our feet and light for our path" (Psalm 119:105).

Reflect on a recent time of experiencing Scripture:

- Romans 15:7—*I recently expressed Christ-like acceptance to _____ _____ when _____.*

- Proverbs 15:1—*I recently shared a gentle response in the face of anger when _____.*

- James 5:16—*I recently apologized to _____ concerning _____.*

- Romans 12:15a—*I recently was able to rejoice with _____ over _____.*

- Romans 12:15b—*I recently was able to mourn with _____ over _____.*

- Other:_____

Celebrate with a partner or small group over your recent walk in the light of God's Word. Allow the Holy Spirit to prompt you to ask yourself often, *"What Bible verses did I experience today?"*

Walking in the Light of God's People

Through Faithful Engagement in Fellowship

"Loving me empowers you to obey my commands" (John 14:15).

L3

Experiencing God as He really is through deepened intimacy with Him

Some of us view God as an *inspecting* god. As you read the verse, you may have imagined a tone of expectation and demand. The words might carry a questioning tone, conveying the sense that there is a test to be passed or a measurement to be taken. You may have even imagined your inspecting god shaking his finger at you as he speaks these words. His stern tone and gestures warn of his constant inspection.

Some of us may view God as *disappointed* in us. As you read John 14:15, you may have heard a voice that seemed full of dissatisfaction. This kind of god might look down at you with arms crossed, shaking his head as he says: "If you really loved me, then you would be able to keep my commandments. In fact, I have known all along that you did not really love me, and what you just did proves it!"

Some of us may see God as a *distant* god. As you read the verse above, the voice you heard may have seemed cold or disinterested. A distant god would speak the verse with halfhearted enthusiasm or great indifference. This kind of god might seem preoccupied with other things or other more important people. You might picture him looking up absentmindedly and saying: "Oh, if you love me, then you will probably keep my commandments. Thanks for stopping by."

Consider the wonder that this verse may be a promise in a long line of promises! (See John 14:2, 3, 12, 13, and 14). Could it be when you woke up this morning, God was looking down longing for you to love Him, knowing that as you do, you'll then keep His commandments? **The real Jesus is not inspecting, disappointed, or distant. He's excited to share in your love!**

A life of abundance finds encouragement and freedom to live as an *awakening catalyst* through engaging fellowship with other Jesus followers.

Pause to first reflect on how, at times, you might not see God as "excited to love you:"

Sadly at times, I view God incorrectly as _____
(inspecting, disappointed, distant, or other).

Now share this with a partner or small group and then take turns praying for one another that the Holy Spirit would bring freedom to embrace Christ as He really is—exited to love you!

Celebrate together that as you awaken each morning, He is longing to share with you His love and caring involvement.

L3

Experiencing God as
He really is through
deepened intimacy
with Him

> LOVE THE LORD YOUR GOD WITH ALL YOUR HEART, SOUL AND MIND
>
> ...and love your neighbor as you love yourself. The whole law and the prophets depend on these two commandments" (Matthew 22:37–40 NASB).

REREAD JOHN 15 EACH DAY REFLECTING ON A DIFFERENT ASPECT OF HIS LOVE.

DAY 1

SPIRIT EMPOWERED *Faith*

L3

Experiencing God as He really is through deepened intimacy with Him

I. **Reflect on how the REAL God is a God of love.** How might this text lead me to better love God? "We love because He first loved us" (1 John 4:19 NASB). We can only love the REAL God with all our "heart, soul, mind, and strength."

A. As you read and reflect on the chapter, how might you describe the REAL God as He is seen as Father, Son, and Holy Spirit?

1. In verse ___1___, He is seen as _True Vine, Son_

2. In verse ___1___, He is seen as _GARDNER, FATHER_

3. In verse ___9___, the love of Jesus is seen toward _Disciple_ as He _loves us as Father loved Him_

4. In verse ___11___ the love of Jesus is seen toward _Disciple_ as He _tells us that His joy my be in us._

5. How might these insights challenge some of your misconceptions of God?

Sadly, I sometimes mistakenly see God as _Joyless —_

DAY 2

SPIRIT EMPOWERED *Faith*

W1

Frequently being led by the Spirit into deeper love for the One who wrote the Word

B. **Reflect on how God has loved *you* since He is the same yesterday, today, and forever (Hebrews 13:8). Pause to let Him love you.**

1. *Father, as you express yourself to me as the God who _____ _____, my heart is moved with _____.*

2. *Father, as you express yourself to me as the God who _____ _____, my heart is moved with _____.*

C. Jesus is available to love you like we read of His love in this chapter. Pause to express your heart to Him as you see Him in this chapter.

1. Describe how Jesus has loved you in some of the same ways that you read of His love in this chapter:

I have experienced the love of Jesus as He has _____ _____.

2. *Jesus, as you love me like you loved those in this chapter, my heart is touched with _____.*

DAY 3

P5

Ministering His life and love to our nearest ones at home and with family as well as faithful engagement in His body, the church

---

II. **Reflect on how you can better love your "near ones."** How might this text lead me to better love others? "As I have loved you, so you also should love one another." (John 13:34 NASB).

Since we have freely received of His love, we are to freely give this same love to others. Consider again how you see love portrayed in this chapter.

A. Who among your family or friends might you better love?

1. *I could better love_____,*
   especially by _____.

DAY 4

M1

Imparting the gospel and one's very life in daily activities and relationships, vocation and community

---

B. **Reflect on how you might be a witness of His love.** Notice again how Jesus expressed love by accepting, forgiving, or sacrificing? How might Jesus have taken initiative, expressed compassion, offered support, shared truth, and eternal hope?

1. Who in the traffic patterns of your life might benefit from receiving the blessing of Christ's love through you?
   (Who)_____could benefit from my sharing the love
   of Jesus by _____.

2. Who in your life could benefit from sharing part of your life story of encountering truth and eternal hope?
   (Who)_____could benefit from my sharing more of
   _____.

3. Pause now to pray for this person and then for yourself as you impart both your life and the gospel.

DAY 5

L4

Rejoicing regularly in my identity as "His Beloved"

III. **Reflect on *you* as the recipient of His love.** Your significance, value, and worth have been established by your Creator through the gift of His Son. How might this text affirm your identity as "His Beloved"?

"The light of God's love shined within us when he sent his matchless Son into the world so that we might live through him." (1 John 4:9).

Celebrate how you have received His love and grace, His forgiveness and new life, His calling and kingdom purpose.

A. Reread the text as His truth being shared just for you.

1. *I'm grateful that I have experienced the blessing of verse _____*
   as I _____.

B. Since He is the same yesterday, today, and forever, meditate on your being *in* the story of this chapter. Allow Him to love you as you read of His love in the chapter.

1. *My heart is touched with gratitude that Jesus _____*
   _____.

Walking in the Light of God's Son

Through Fresh Encounters With Jesus   John 12:35; John 8:12

"I am a true sprouting vine, and the farmer who tends the vine is my Father. He cares for the branches connected to me by lifting and propping up the fruitless branches and pruning every fruitful branch to yield a greater harvest" (John 15:1–2).

M10

Living submissively within His body, the church as instruction and encouragement, reproof and correction are graciously received by faithful disciples

Lifting…propping up the fruitless…pruning every fruitful branch to yield a greater harvest. This is an often misunderstood scripture, except for the One who tends the vine. He knows what to do when a branch is found beaten to the ground after a storm. He lifts it out of the mud and carefully washes the mud from the leaves. Otherwise, the branch will die, and there will be no fruit.

Next, He intertwines the branch among the stronger vines, propping it up out of the dirt. The few leaves and twigs that are too damaged, He carefully clips away to save the vine. A harvest is then possible. In fact, a harvest is then guaranteed.

Some would have you believe that Jesus comes through the vineyard cutting and slicing away every damaged and muddied branch. If you don't clean up your act, you're cut off at the stem and thrown on the burn pile. But that is not the case. This is certainly not the character of the Savior that the church has known. There is no fear in His love because perfect love casts out all fear (1 John 4:18–19).

Which are you? The perfect and healthy trailing vine that runs across the trestle with beauty and grace, or the one who has fallen, face down in the mud, needing the help and expertise of the Master Gardener?

See Him now. He lifts the fallen. He cleans the wound. He touches the leper and speaks life to the dead. No reason to fear. No reason to hide.

Just tell Him. *Jesus I have fallen—again. I need your kind hand of mercy to lift me from this muddy path. Thank you that I have nothing to fear. You intended for me to produce fruit, and by your grace, my life will do just that.*

Walking in the Light of God's People

"So this is my command: Love each other deeply, as much as I have loved you. For the greatest love of all is a love that sacrifices all. And this great love is demonstrated when a person sacrifices his life for his friends" (John 15:12–13).

SPIRIT EMPOWERED *Faith*

M10

Living submissively within His body, the church, as instruction and encouragement, reproof and correction are graciously received by faithful disciples

The lazy flame of the oil lamps cast more shadows than light as the twelve huddle around the low table. Beneath the open windows, the city breaths out life and commerce, the noise carried by a slight breeze that tempers the stale air. You can smell the scents from the street mixing now with the sweat of the men and the simple meal prepared for the Master. They are dirty from the feet up.

Everything has changed. On the walk from Jericho, He had been so focused. What was supposed to be triumph when He entered the city, turned to tears as He wept over the same. The words He speaks now are distilled down to a profound whisper as they bend in to catch every word. The years of teaching and preaching come to light in the dim glow of the room. "Love each other as I have loved you," He says. It is a living command. It is what separates His church from all others.

Is this really possible? Practical? Doable? Only by first experiencing the kind of love that Jesus demands is this possible. "This is my command." It is not a suggestion or an encouragement. It is the marching orders for the followers of Jesus from this final night and going forward to His second return. There is no place on earth that this kind of love is lived out like in the church of Jesus Christ. Whether in a church service or small meeting in a home, bonds are formed that exemplify what Jesus commanded. The body of Christ is knit together by every ligament with which it is equipped, as each part is working properly and promotes the body's growth in building itself up in love (Ephesians 4:16).

- Who has God uniquely bound you to?

- What saint has become a friend closer than a brother?

Stop and thank God with a partner or small group that you are not alone because of that friend.

- What grace does your friend express that is a blessing to you?

- Some examples are truth-telling, mercy, joy, or encouragement.

Now follow up by engaging your friend with words like this:

Recently, the Holy Spirit has reminded me of what a gift you have been to my life. I am most grateful that you are _____ (merciful, joy-filled, encouraging) to me.

Walking in the Light of God's Word

Through Frequent Experience of Scripture   John 12:35; Psalm 119:105

"I call you my most intimate friends, for I reveal to you everything that I've heard from my Father" (John 15:15).

How deeply intimate and far-reaching is His love! How enduring and inclusive it is! Endless love beyond measurement, beyond academic knowledge—this extravagant love pours into you until you are filled to overflowing with the fullness of God! (see Ephesians 3:17–10)

What do best friends share? Everything.

The final evening before the passion would begin, Jesus bared His sinless soul to those who He knew would betray, doubt, and run away in fear. John 13:1 begins, "Jesus knowing." He who knew no sin also knew the heart of every man. He released Judas to "go and do what you will do quickly." He told the truth to Peter. "You will deny me three times." He washed the feet of every disciple, the same feet that would run away to protect themselves.

"I have never called you 'servants,' because a master doesn't confide in his servants, and servants don't always understand what the master is doing. But I call you my most intimate friends, for I reveal to you everything that I've heard from my Father" (John 15:15).

No doubt, it will seem strange, but friendship with God is foundational to our being a good friend to others. The startling possibility that you and I (the created) can relate closely, even intimately, with the Creator is hard to grasp, but it's true. The Bible says that Moses spoke with God as with a friend, and Abraham is referred to as a "friend of God" (Exodus 33:11; James 2:23). In the New Testament, as we encounter the God-Man Jesus, this possibility of friendship seems closer and more possible.

The apostle James reminds us that our "friendship with the world" will hinder our friendship with the Lord (James 4:4). In fact, God is a "jealous" friend, knowing that our friendship with the world will bring pain, while our intimacy with Him brings blessings.

M10

Living submissively within His body, the church as instruction and encouragement, reproof and correction are graciously received by faithful disciples

True friendship, which is learned in our relationship with the Lord, brings blessings:

- **Friends deeply know one another**—He knows you, and you make a priority of knowing Him (Jeremiah 1:5; Philippians 3:8).

- **Friends initiate care for one another**—He meets needs, speaks with you, stays committed to you (Psalm 37:25; 85:8; 139:3; Philippians 4:19). You listen to what He says, try not to grieve Him, and celebrate His goodness toward you (1 Samuel 3:9; Psalm 100:2; Ephesians 4:30).

- **Friends vulnerably trust one another**—In Scripture, Christ shares His joys, hurts, and hopes (John 15:11, 18; 17:5). You share with Him your joys, hurts, and hopes (Jeremiah 33:3; Romans 8:26).

On and on, the Master served His friends. He shared everything with those He chose to love. He chose to love you as well. Will you choose to receive everything from Him? **Pray like this:** *"Lord, you have chosen to love me completely! I am so grateful for your great love and now receive it gratefully. Jesus, I want the kind of relationship with you that you spoke of in your word. I want you, Jesus, as my closest friend."*

EACH OF THE FOUR GOSPELS ARE WRITTEN TO A PECULIAR POPULATION. Matthew wrote to the Jewish church, and his gospel reflects the first century church that resided in Israel as well as the diaspora that began before the fall of Jerusalem in 70 AD. Mark's is the power gospel—short, power-driven, and fast moving. He was speaking to the rulers of the world, the Romans who controlled everyone except the fledging church that could not be contained. Mark declares that no one on this earth is more powerful than Jesus. Luke's influence was far more reaching. His gospel as wells as Acts were written to everyman, declaring Jesus as the Savior of the Jewish and Gentile world alike.

Enter John's gospel that transcends population and captures the heart of God for His creation. John wrote to the soul of humankind, a soul left adrift from the garden of Eden forward, whose tattered sail was none the less filled with the sovereign breath of the Spirit that guided all of prophecy to a Bethlehem cave. Again, John appealed to the soul of humankind that longed for home. Instead of facts, he tells of the passionate love of God. He entered into the very world He created, yet the world was unaware. He came to the very people He created—to those who should have recognized Him, but they did not receive Him. But those who embraced Him, and took hold of His name were given the authority to become who they really were—the children of God! (see John 1:10–12)

SPIRIT
EMPOWERED
Faith

M10

Living submissively within His body, the church as instruction and encouragement, reproof and correction are graciously received by faithful disciples

God to chang

we are bette

In this seri

Sin, Tempt

Freedom ar

WE

When we fal

know how to

begin to mov

> **LOVE THE LORD YOUR GOD WITH ALL YOUR HEART, SOUL AND MIND**
> …and love your neighbor as you love yourself. The whole law and the prophets depend on these two commandments" (Matthew 22:37–40 NASB).

REREAD JOHN 16 EACH DAY REFLECTING ON A DIFFERENT ASPECT OF HIS LOVE.

DAY 1

L3

Experiencing God as He really is through deepened intimacy with Him

I. **Reflect on how the REAL God is a God of love.** How might this text lead me to better love God? "We love because He first loved us" (1 John 4:19 NASB). We can only love the REAL God with all our "heart, soul, mind, and strength."

A. As you read and reflect on the chapter, how might you describe the REAL God as He is seen as Father, Son, and Holy Spirit?

1. In verse_____, He is seen as _____
_____.

2. In verse _____, He is seen as _____
_____.

3. In verse _____, the love of Jesus is seen toward_____
as He _____.

4. In verse _____, the love of Jesus is seen toward_____
as He _____.

5. How might these insights challenge some of your misconceptions of God?

Sadly, I sometimes mistakenly see God as _____
_____.

DAY 2

W1

Frequently being led by the Spirit into deeper love for the One who wrote the Word

B. **Reflect on how God has loved *you*** since He is the same yesterday, today, and forever (Hebrews 13:8). **Pause to let Him love you.**

1. *Father, as you express yourself to me as the God who _____*
_____, my heart is moved with
_____.

2. *Father, as you express yourself to me as the God who _____*
_____, my heart is moved with
_____.

C. Jesus is available to love you like we read of His love in this chapter. Pause to express your heart to Him as you see Him in this chapter.

1. Describe how Jesus has loved you in some of the same ways that you read of His love in this chapter:

I have experienced the love of Jesus as He has _____
_____.

2. *Jesus, as you love me like you loved those in this chapter, my heart is touched with _____.*

DAY 3

P5

Ministering His life and love to our nearest ones at home and with family as well as faithful engagement in His body, the church

II. **Reflect on how you can better love your "near ones."** How might this text lead me to better love others? "As I have loved you, so you also should love one another." (John 13:34 NASB).

Since we have freely received of His love, we are to freely give this same love to others. Consider again how you see love portrayed in this chapter.

A. Who among your family or friends might you better love?

1. *I could better love_____,*
    especially by _____.

DAY 4

M1

Imparting the gospel and one's very life in daily activities and relationships, vocation and community

B. **Reflect on how you might be a witness of His love.** Notice again how Jesus expressed love by accepting, forgiving, or sacrificing? How might Jesus have taken initiative, expressed compassion, offered support, shared truth, and eternal hope?

1. Who in the traffic patterns of your life might benefit from receiving the blessing of Christ's love through you?
    (Who)_____could benefit from my sharing the love of Jesus by _____.

2. Who in your life could benefit from sharing part of your life story of encountering truth and eternal hope?
    (Who)_____could benefit from my sharing more of
    _____.

3. Pause now to pray for this person and then for yourself as you impart both your life and the gospel.

DAY 5

L4

Rejoicing regularly in my identity as "His Beloved"

III. **Reflect on *you* as the recipient of His love.** Your significance, value, and worth have been established by your Creator through the gift of His Son. How might this text affirm your identity as "His Beloved"?

"The light of God's love shined within us when he sent his matchless Son into the world so that we might live through him." (1 John 4:9).

Celebrate how you have received His love and grace, His forgiveness and new life, His calling and kingdom purpose.

A. Reread the text as His truth being shared just for you.

1. *I'm grateful that I have experienced the blessing of verse _____*
    as I _____.

B. Since He is the same yesterday, today, and forever, meditate on your being *in* the story of this chapter. Allow Him to love you as you read of His love in the chapter.

1. *My heart is touched with gratitude that Jesus _____*
    _____.

Walking in the Light of God's Word

Through Frequent Experience of Scripture   John 12:35; Psalm 119:105

"But here's the truth: it's to your advantage that I go away; for if I don't go away, the Divine Encourager will not be released to you. But after I depart, I will send him to you" (John 16:7).

W1

Frequently being led by the Spirit into deeper love for the One who wrote the Word

God wants us to live abundantly "in the present" as His Word brings healing to hurt, anger, guilt, fear, and condemnation, which are heart hindrances to life abundant. In John 16, Jesus encourages His disciples not to surrender to confusion or doubt (John 16:1).

For the benefit of His disciples, He sends the Divine Encourager: "But here's the truth: it's to your advantage that I go away; for if I don't go away, the Divine Encourager will not be released to you. But after I depart, I will send him to you" (John 16:7).

God wants to take us from a place of sadness to joy! Jesus uses a powerful metaphor to reinforce this truth: "Just like a woman giving birth experiences intense labor pains in delivering her baby, yet after the child is born she quickly forgets what she went through because of the overwhelming joy of knowing that a new baby has been born into the world"(John 16:21).

Jesus goes on to encourage His disciples with these words: "So will you also pass through a time of intense sorrow when I am taken from you, but you will see me again! And then your hearts will burst with joy, with no one being able to take it from you!" (John 16:22).

"When the people heard the letter read out loud, they were overjoyed and delighted by its encouraging message" (Acts 15:31). Use the words of Scripture to encourage one another.

- Within your group, share a Scripture that has *come alive* in your heart to guide and shape your life: *"I remember how I felt insecure about my relationship with God until He brought reassurance to my heart through 1 John 5:13."*

- Pray together with a group member, thanking God for the encouragement of His Word: *Thank you, Lord, for helping me to experience freedom from fear and to have more overwhelming joy in my life.*

Walking in the Light of God's People

Through Faithful Engagement in Fellowship   John 12:35; Matthew 5:14

"Jesus replied, 'Now you finally believe in me'" (John 16:31).

John 16 illustrates the Jesus strategy for relational legacy: belong, become, and believe. If we reverse this order, we might face challenges to leaving a relational legacy. First, we might seek to defend the truth more than demonstrate it. Second, we might try to explain more than express. Finally, we might seek to impress others, rather than impart life to them.

Let's consider how we might lead as Jesus led by creating a relational legacy of…

- **Belonging**—"You will go directly to the Father and ask him for anything you desire and he will give it to you, because of your relationship with me" (John 16:23). Jesus invites and includes His disciples to do life together—imparting life and love to them.

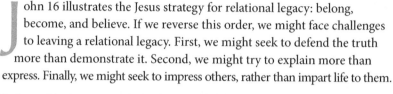

- **Becoming**—"Until now you've not been bold enough to ask the Father for a single thing in my name, but now you can ask, and keep on asking him! And you can be sure that you'll receive what you ask for, and your joy will have no limits!" (John 16:24). Jesus models an instinctive, attractive, and contagious lifestyle to His disciples.

- **Believing**—"Jesus replied, 'Now you finally believe in me'" (John 16:31). The disciples of Jesus believe in Him as the Spirit makes Him known.

SPIRIT EMPOWERED
Faith

W1

Frequently being led by the Spirit into deeper love for the One who wrote the Word

Pause and assess how you and your team are leading others in…

- **Belonging** to a community of Jesus followers. Is there freedom within your group to express humility, exercise faith, and experience intimacy? How might you advance a culture of belonging?

- **Becoming** like Jesus who you follow. Consider how you might advance a culture of becoming a people who are characterized as compassionate, vulnerable, humble, grateful, and giving first to others.

- **Believing** in Jesus as the Spirit makes Him known. Consider how you might support a culture of attentive listening to others' story, vulnerably sharing your story, and sensitive witness of Jesus' story.

Then pray together with a partner or small group:

Dear Jesus, help us to lead as you led by creating a relational legacy through a process of belonging to you, becoming like you, and believing in you.

Walking in the Light of God's Son

Through Fresh Encounters With Jesus   John 12:35; John 8:12

"For in this unbelieving world you will experience trouble and sorrows, but you must be courageous for I have conquered the world!" (John 16:33).

W1

Frequently being led by the Spirit into deeper love for the One who wrote the Word

Hurt is inevitable. It's not a matter of if we're going to be hurt, but rather when we are hurt in this life, what are we going to do about it? Hurt can come from many sources: circumstances (illness, accidents), family members (parents, siblings, grandparents), friends, teachers, coaches, enemies.

Hurt also takes many forms. Synonyms for hurt or trouble in this world might include:

- I was disappointed that my teammate didn't complete his part of the project.
- I felt rejected when my teenager wouldn't reciprocate affection.
- I was embarrassed when I tripped and fell with many onlookers.
- I felt betrayed when my friend spoke against me.
- I was frustrated when my car wouldn't start.
- I felt abandoned when my dad left our family.
- I felt sad on the anniversary of my mother's death.

Consider your pain; it's real; don't minimize it. Your pain is important to Jesus. It's significant that we have a great High Priest who empathizes with us, having suffered as we suffer (Hebrews 4:14–16).

- Rejected in his hometown (Mark 6:2–4)
- Called demon-possessed by the Pharisees (John 10:20)
- Rejected by His family (Mark 3:20–21)
- Insulted by His disciples (Matthew 26:6–9)
- Disappointed by Philip (John 14:6–9)
- Offended in the upper room at the last supper (Luke 22:24)
- Unsupported in the garden of Gethsemane (Mark 14:32–40)
- Embarrassed on the cross (John 19:23)
- Mocked (Luke 23:36)
- Cursed (Luke 23:39)

Pause and reflect on Jesus' suffering.

He was "A man of sorrows and acquainted with grief"(Isaiah 53:3 NASB). Allow yourself to fellowship with the sufferings of Jesus (see Philippians 3:10). **Express your care:** *Lord, because I love you, it makes me sad that you have experienced so much pain.*

Frequently being led by
the Spirit into deeper love
for the One who wrote
the Word

> **LOVE THE LORD YOUR GOD WITH ALL YOUR HEART, SOUL AND MIND**
>
> ...and love your neighbor as you love yourself. The whole law and the prophets depend on these two commandments" (Matthew 22:37–40 NASB).

John 17

REREAD JOHN 17 EACH DAY REFLECTING ON A DIFFERENT ASPECT OF HIS LOVE.

DAY 1

L3

Experiencing God as He really is through deepened intimacy with Him

I. **Reflect on how the REAL God is a God of love.** How might this text lead me to better love God? "We love because He first loved us" (1 John 4:19 NASB). We can only love the REAL God with all our "heart, soul, mind, and strength."

A. As you read and reflect on the chapter, how might you describe the REAL God as He is seen as Father, Son, and Holy Spirit?

1. In verse_____, He is seen as _____
   _____.

2. In verse _____, He is seen as _____
   _____.

3. In verse _____, the love of Jesus is seen toward_____
   as He _____.

4. In verse _____, the love of Jesus is seen toward_____
   as He _____.

5. How might these insights challenge some of your misconceptions of God?

   Sadly, I sometimes mistakenly see God as _____
   _____.

DAY 2

W1

Frequently being led by the Spirit into deeper love for the One who wrote the Word

B. **Reflect on how God has loved *you*** since He is the same yesterday, today, and forever (Hebrews 13:8). **Pause to let Him love you.**

1. *Father, as you express yourself to me as the God who* _____
   _____, *my heart is moved with*
   _____.

2. *Father, as you express yourself to me as the God who* _____
   _____, *my heart is moved with*
   _____.

C. Jesus is available to love you like we read of His love in this chapter. Pause to express your heart to Him as you see Him in this chapter.

1. Describe how Jesus has loved you in some of the same ways that you read of His love in this chapter:

   I have experienced the love of Jesus as He has _____
   _____.

2. *Jesus, as you love me like you loved those in this chapter, my heart is touched with* _____.

DAY 3

P5

Ministering His life and love to our nearest ones at home and with family as well as faithful engagement in His body, the church

II. **Reflect on how you can better love your "near ones."** How might this text lead me to better love others? "As I have loved you, so you also should love one another." (John 13:34 NASB).

Since we have freely received of His love, we are to freely give this same love to others. Consider again how you see love portrayed in this chapter.

A. Who among your family or friends might you better love?

1. *I could better love_____,*
   especially by _____.

DAY 4

M1

Imparting the gospel and one's very life in daily activities and relationships, vocation and community

B. **Reflect on how you might be a witness of His love.** Notice again how Jesus expressed love by accepting, forgiving, or sacrificing? How might Jesus have taken initiative, expressed compassion, offered support, shared truth, and eternal hope?

1. Who in the traffic patterns of your life might benefit from receiving the blessing of Christ's love through you?
   (Who)_____could benefit from my sharing the love of Jesus by _____.

2. Who in your life could benefit from sharing part of your life story of encountering truth and eternal hope?
   (Who)_____could benefit from my sharing more of
   _____.

3. Pause now to pray for this person and then for yourself as you impart both your life and the gospel.

DAY 5

L4

Rejoicing regularly in my identity as "His Beloved"

III. **Reflect on *you* as the recipient of His love.** Your significance, value, and worth have been established by your Creator through the gift of His Son. How might this text affirm your identity as "His Beloved"?

"The light of God's love shined within us when he sent his matchless Son into the world so that we might live through him." (1 John 4:9).

Celebrate how you have received His love and grace, His forgiveness and new life, His calling and kingdom purpose.

A. Reread the text as His truth being shared just for you.

1. *I'm grateful that I have experienced the blessing of verse _____*
   as I _____.

B. Since He is the same yesterday, today, and forever, meditate on your being *in* the story of this chapter. Allow Him to love you as you read of His love in the chapter.

1. *My heart is touched with gratitude that Jesus _____*
   _____.

Walking in the Light of God's Son

Through Fresh Encounters With Jesus   John 12:35; John 8:12

"Eternal life means to know and experience you as the only true God, and to know and experience Jesus Christ, as the Son whom you have sent" (John 17:3).

L8

Disciplined, bold, and believing prayer

The sounds of the city faded with the light of day. A chill crept slowly through the room with a foreboding the men had not sensed before. Something had changed.

Jesus kept talking about leaving them alone, going where they could not follow, persecution and hatred arriving. What had been an exciting stream of divine truth was building to a torrent of disturbing revelation.

The words seemed to thicken the very air they breathed. Then, for a moment, He grew silent. His gaze went beyond anything seen in the darkness of the room, and He began to pray, "Father the time has come."

Certainly they had seen Him pray before. He had even taught them what to say when they prayed. Mostly though, they had watched Him leave and go off by Himself. Someone would follow, just to make sure He was safe you understand, and they would report the other-worldliness of the scene as the Son talked to His Father.

Now, in a way they had never witnessed. He prayed to the Father with them fully present and engaged. Heaven descended into the room.

"Eternal life means to know and experience you as the only true God, and to know and experience Jesus Christ, as the Son whom you have sent" (John 17:3).

Eternal life. Beyond the day to day of business as usual, beyond the growing old, beyond the grave, there had always been the mystery of eternity. Now, in these last hours before He would leave. He told them the truth human-kind had begged to hear.

Eternal life is to know and experience the Father and Jesus Christ, whom He sent. It is so simple that most make it more than difficult. To know the Father is to know the Son. To know the Son is to invite Him into your Life. To invite Him in means to admit that you desperately need Him.

We all do. No one is exempt because man was not created to be alone and apart from God. Not ever. Not now. Certainly not in eternity. Jesus came so you could know and experience both the Father and the Son.

Do you need Him now? Pray like this.

Jesus, more than anything else, I need to know that you are with me and for me right now. With all of my heart, I want to experience the love of God that you came to earth to show. I ask you to fill the void in my heart that can only be filled by you. Now speak to me, Jesus, and I will obey.

Walking in the Light of God's Word

Through Frequent Experience of Scripture   John 12:35; Psalm 119:105

"I have commissioned them to represent me just as you commissioned me to represent You. And now I dedicate Myself to them as a holy sacrifice so that they will live as fully dedicated to God and be made holy by Your truth" (John 17:18–19).

L8

Disciplined, bold, and believing prayer

esus dedicated Himself as the sacrifice for both sin and transformation… SO THAT we might become something that we are not…SO THAT the church would have the power to completely dedicate time, resource and energy to kingdom advancement…SO THAT every person who received Jesus would be sanctified and made holy by the truth that lived within through the Person of the Holy Spirit.

His prayer was not just thoughtfully constructed sentences that felt good, but truth that when embraced would come alive in "rivers of living water (bursting) from within you" (John 7:38).

Pause and reflect on Jesus' suffering.

He was "A man of sorrows and acquainted with grief" (Isaiah 53:3 NASB). Allow yourself to fellowship with the sufferings of Jesus (see Philippians 3:10). **Express your care:** *"Lord, because I love you, it makes me sad that you have experienced so much pain."*

When Jesus promises, He delivers. Do you need to experience living water right now? What part of your character needs to be washed and made holy? What area of life needs living water applied?

Pray like this:

Jesus, today I need to experience the truth of your Word that my life would be dedicated and made holy by your truth. You promised that your truth would not be burdensome but instead bring freedom. You said your truth would set me free! I need that freedom, cleansing, and empowering in _____

_____

(my character, failure, marriage, discipline), and I give you permission to speak that truth that will change me. I commit to submit, Jesus. Now come in power in my life.

Walking in the Light of God's People

Through Faithful Engagement in Fellowship   John 12:35; Matthew 5:14

"And I ask not only for these disciples, but also for all those who will one day believe in me through their message. I pray for them all to be joined together as one even as you and I, Father, are joined together as one. I pray for them to become one with us so that the world will recognize that you sent me" (John 17:20–21).

L8

Disciplined, bold, and believing prayer

O ver and over throughout the evening, Jesus had said, "Ask the Father…Ask in my name…He will not refuse you!"

Now He asks; He prays. The One who promised that His name would shatter the ceiling between heaven and earth, the One who promised that requests in His name would resonate throughout the throne room of God, He prays. His prayer will not be refused.

- He prays for all believers throughout the centuries until His second return. Verse 20 records that this prayer is not just for these eleven disciples but also "for those who will believe in me through their word."

- He prays that we would be in unity.

- He prays that the unity would emulate the fellowship of the Father, Son, and Holy Spirit.

Though often ignored, the reason He prays is "So that the world will recognize that you sent me."

Imagine this most sacred time in the upper room in Jerusalem. The Passover meal is finished. The Servant Christ has washed the feet of each disciple, and the betrayer has departed to complete his betrayal of the Messiah. Christ will soon be arrested, crucified, and buried. Three days later, He will rise from the dead, but now He prays!

During these final moments together, Christ and His now eleven disciples must complete preparations for His death and for their leadership of the early church. Christ will provide instruction, encouragement, and hope in this "Upper Room Discourse," culminating in His longest recorded prayer (John 13–17). It is during this John 17 prayer that we also see the personal relevance to our lives.

Are you one of His disciples? If not, pause quietly even now to invite Him into your life: *Lord Jesus, thanks for loving me, praying for me, and desiring a relationship with me. I need you to forgive me and change me as you come into my life to make me part of your family. Thank you for doing so, even now. By faith, I receive you as my Savior and Lord.*

Please stop and read verses 20 and 21 again. Christ has declared a critical ingredient in our lives as we follow Him: that we would live in oneness—without division, strife, jealously, or pride—being diligent to mutually care for, yield to, and love one another (1 Corinthians 12:24–27; Ephesians 5:21; Galatians 5:13). The divine results will be: "that the world may believe!" (John 17:21).

The greatest tool of evangelism is the unity the church shares. That also means that the greatest detriment to people coming to Christ is disunity. Jealousy, bitterness, pride, and other unity-breakers keep souls from heaven and deliver souls to hell. **Now, pray together this way:** *Father, in order to fulfill your desire and the prayer of Jesus, I ask you to give me more (patience, faith, forbearance, grace) to fulfill your desires for unity. I ask you to change me and let my life be an answer to your prayer.*

L8

Disciplined, bold, and believing prayer

> LOVE THE LORD YOUR GOD WITH ALL YOUR HEART, SOUL AND MIND
>
> …and love your neighbor as you love yourself. The whole law and the prophets depend on these two commandments" (Matthew 22:37–40 NASB).

REREAD JOHN 18 EACH DAY REFLECTING ON A DIFFERENT ASPECT OF HIS LOVE.

DAY 1

SPIRIT EMPOWERED
Faith

L3

Experiencing God as He really is through deepened intimacy with Him

I. **Reflect on how the REAL God is a God of love.** How might this text lead me to better love God? "We love because He first loved us" (1 John 4:19 NASB). We can only love the REAL God with all our "heart, soul, mind, and strength."

A. As you read and reflect on the chapter, how might you describe the REAL God as He is seen as Father, Son, and Holy Spirit?

1. In verse_____, He is seen as _____
   _____.

2. In verse _____, He is seen as _____
   _____.

3. In verse _____, the love of Jesus is seen toward_____
   as He _____.

4. In verse _____, the love of Jesus is seen toward_____
   as He _____.

5. How might these insights challenge some of your misconceptions of God?

   Sadly, I sometimes mistakenly see God as _____
   _____.

DAY 2

SPIRIT EMPOWERED
Faith

W1

Frequently being led by the Spirit into deeper love for the One who wrote the Word

B. **Reflect on how God has loved *you*** since He is the same yesterday, today, and forever (Hebrews 13:8). **Pause to let Him love you.**

1. *Father, as you express yourself to me as the God who* _____
   _____, *my heart is moved with*
   _____.

2. *Father, as you express yourself to me as the God who* _____
   _____, *my heart is moved with*
   _____.

C. Jesus is available to love you like we read of His love in this chapter. Pause to express your heart to Him as you see Him in this chapter.

1. Describe how Jesus has loved you in some of the same ways that you read of His love in this chapter:

   I have experienced the love of Jesus as He has _____
   _____.

2. *Jesus, as you love me like you loved those in this chapter, my heart is touched with* _____.

DAY 3

Ministering His life and love to our nearest ones at home and with family as well as faithful engagement in His body, the church

II. **Reflect on how you can better love your "near ones."** How might this text lead me to better love others? "As I have loved you, so you also should love one another." (John 13:34 NASB).

Since we have freely received of His love, we are to freely give this same love to others. Consider again how you see love portrayed in this chapter.

A. Who among your family or friends might you better love?

1. *I could better love_____,*
   especially by _____.

DAY 4

Imparting the gospel and one's very life in daily activities and relationships, vocation and community

B. **Reflect on how you might be a witness of His love.** Notice again how Jesus expressed love by accepting, forgiving, or sacrificing? How might Jesus have taken initiative, expressed compassion, offered support, shared truth, and eternal hope?

1. Who in the traffic patterns of your life might benefit from receiving the blessing of Christ's love through you?
   (Who)_____could benefit from my sharing the love of Jesus by _____.

2. Who in your life could benefit from sharing part of your life story of encountering truth and eternal hope?
   (Who)_____could benefit from my sharing more of _____.

3. Pause now to pray for this person and then for yourself as you impart both your life and the gospel.

DAY 5

Rejoicing regularly in my identity as "His Beloved"

III. **Reflect on *you* as the recipient of His love.** Your significance, value, and worth have been established by your Creator through the gift of His Son. How might this text affirm your identity as "His Beloved"?

"The light of God's love shined within us when he sent his matchless Son into the world so that we might live through him." (1 John 4:9).

Celebrate how you have received His love and grace, His forgiveness and new life, His calling and kingdom purpose.

A. Reread the text as His truth being shared just for you.

1. *I'm grateful that I have experienced the blessing of verse _____*
   as I _____.

B. Since He is the same yesterday, today, and forever, meditate on your being *in* the story of this chapter. Allow Him to love you as you read of His love in the chapter.

1. *My heart is touched with gratitude that Jesus _____*
   _____.

Walking in the Light of God's Word

Through Frequent Experience of Scripture   John 12:35; Psalm 119:105

"He said this to fulfill the prophecy he had spoken, 'Father, not one of those you have given me has been lost'"(John 18:9).

He said this to fulfill the prophecy he had spoken, "Father, not one of those you have given me has been lost" (John 18:9).

As certain as this declaration was, so is every promise of God. As certain as God's faithfulness to this remnant of Jesus followers, so is our security in His promised abundance. "For all of God's promises find their 'yes' of fulfillment in him" (2 Corinthians 1:20 NASB).

Pause now with a partner or in your small group to give thanks for the certainty of His Word. Though every man be found a liar, God remains faithful to fulfill His Word. Thank Him for the certainty of His Word and for the promise of life's abundance as declared by the Son. "I came to give you everything in abundance, more than you expect—life in its fullness until you overflow!" (John 10:10).

Father God, with grateful heart, I cling to your promises for direction in life. Hearing Christ's promise of abundant life gives security and hope. Open the eyes of my heart to see your plans for prospering in whatsoever I do as I walk in the light of your Word (see Psalm 119:105).

SPIRIT EMPOWERED *Faith*

W10

Implicit, unwavering trust that His Word will never fail

Walking in the Light of God's People

Through Faithful Engagement in Fellowship   John 12:35; Matthew 5:14

"As he passed inside, the young servant girl guarding the gate took a look at Peter and said to him, 'Aren't you one of his disciples?' He denied it, saying, 'No! I'm not!'" (John 18:17).

We might be tempted to judge Peter's denial of Jesus harshly until the Holy Spirit shows us ourselves! We are journeying through a world that seems filled with signs of the "latter days" in which:

- People will be lovers of self, focusing on their own plans, needs, and desires.
- People will be lovers of money, giving priority to what they can acquire.
- People will be boastful and arrogant.
- People will be unloving, irreconcilable, and prone to gossip.
- People will be lovers of pleasure.
- There will be only a form of godliness.
- People will indulge the flesh.
- People will become self-willed.
- People will speak arrogant words.
- People will be enticed by fleshly lusts and sensuality, and will become entangled in the world's defilements.

(See 2 Timothy 3:1–5 and 2 Peter 2:10–18 for reference to these characteristics.)

Prayerfully and humbly look at the list again, then respond to the following:

- Consider the weakness of human flesh as we see in ourselves dimensions of "denial" reminiscent of Peter. Which of these characteristics might you struggle with? For example, I sometimes struggle with selfishness when faced with the needs and demands of my family and friends. Which of these symptoms of "denial" might be true for you? *I sometimes struggle with…*

- Now recall the promised certain outcome of Christ's word to Peter: "I have prayed for you, that your faith should not fail, and when you have returned to Me, strengthen your brethren" (Luke 22:32).

- Recall now the personal struggle that you noted earlier. Remember the truth of Hebrews 7:25. We have a great High Priest who, "always lives to make intercession for [us]."

- Pause with your partner or small group to meditate on how Jesus is interceding for you. *"As I reflect on the certainty of God's Word and that Christ prays for me like He did for Peter, my heart is touched with…"*

Share your response with a partner and celebrate with one another that His Word never fails. Ask God to continue to bring fresh encounters with His Spirit that would change, restore, and empower you.

SPIRIT
EMPOWERED
Faith

W10

Implicit, unwavering trust that His Word will never fail

Walking in the Light of God's Son

Through Fresh Encounters With Jesus   John 12:35; John 8:12

"Pilate looked at Jesus and said, 'What is truth?'" (John 18:38).

Imagine for a moment that you are in that hall with Pilate and his prisoner. Imagine the words of the governor's question echoing off the marbled walls of that great hall. Imagine the expression of Pilate's face as he poses the question, scornful at first, then turning serious when the answer does not quickly come.

Seconds tick by. Still the prisoner and the governor study each other. Imagine the governor's thoughts: Who is this Man? Why does He gaze at me so? Picture the prisoner's thoughts: Have I not just told you? I came to bring truth into the world. Pilate, you are looking at the answer to your own question: "I am…the truth" (John 14:6).

Pilate was not just discussing the truth in his Jerusalem palace the day he met Jesus; he was literally looking at it. Truth was standing before him, clothed in human flesh! Jesus Christ is the very embodiment and essence of absolute moral and spiritual truth. "And the Word became flesh and dwelt among us, and we beheld His glory, the glory as of the only begotten of the Father, full of grace and truth" (John 1:14).

Moral and spiritual truth isn't so much a concept as it is a person. It isn't so much something we believe as it is someone we relate to. Moral and spiritual truth has flesh. Thus, truth is not just conceptual; it is intrinsically relational. **Truth is a person!**

SPIRIT
EMPOWERED
Faith

W10

Implicit, unwavering trust that His Word will never fail

To develop God-honoring convictions is to relate intimately to Jesus, the One who is truth. In our daily walk, we have opportunity to reflect the certainty and hope of His Word as we hold tightly to our convictions concerning truth. The strength to do so, however, comes from holding tightly to Jesus the One who is truth!

Take a few moments to consider in your heart the amazing, incredible, wonderful truth that we have been brought into a relationship with the One of whom all these things are true! How does it make you feel to realize that you have the privilege to know, to love, and to be loved by such a Savior, **such a friend?**

Complete this prayer in your own words:

Lord Jesus, as I think about the incredible privilege of having a relationship with you—the Holy One, the All-Powerful One, the Way, the Truth, and the Life, the One who has loved me so sacrificially—my heart is filled with

_____.

(For Example: gratitude, love, joy, praise, peace, awe, or wonder.)

Thank you so very much for loving me and giving me your Word that I might know and follow you. In your name I pray, amen.

JOHN KNEW that the love with which Jesus loved him was not confined to a population but was meant for the hearts of "whosoever would come." His gospel stays true to that theme. Those who read it first for content, doctrine, or apologetics will quickly find themselves confronted with the heights and depths of the love of God for the lost and despised and rejected. Like the disciples, whom the Lord chose from the ghetto of Galilee, the inspired words prove the love of God to all. The very soul of God's creation is John's goal because it was His goal.

SPIRIT
EMPOWERED
Faith
W10

Implicit, unwavering trust that His Word will never fail

> **LOVE THE LORD YOUR GOD WITH ALL YOUR HEART, SOUL AND MIND**
>
> …and love your neighbor as you love yourself. The whole law and the prophets depend on these two commandments" (Matthew 22:37–40 NASB).

REREAD JOHN 19 EACH DAY REFLECTING ON A DIFFERENT ASPECT OF HIS LOVE.

DAY 1

L3

Experiencing God as He really is through deepened intimacy with Him

I. **Reflect on how the REAL God is a God of love.** How might this text lead me to better love God? "We love because He first loved us" (1 John 4:19 NASB). We can only love the REAL God with all our "heart, soul, mind, and strength."

A. As you read and reflect on the chapter, how might you describe the REAL God as He is seen as Father, Son, and Holy Spirit?

1. In verse_____, He is seen as _____
_____.

2. In verse _____, He is seen as _____
_____.

3. In verse _____, the love of Jesus is seen toward_____
as He _____.

4. In verse _____, the love of Jesus is seen toward_____
as He _____.

5. How might these insights challenge some of your misconceptions of God?

Sadly, I sometimes mistakenly see God as _____
_____.

DAY 2

W1

Frequently being led by the Spirit into deeper love for the One who wrote the Word

B. Reflect on how God has loved *you* since He is the same yesterday, today, and forever (Hebrews 13:8). **Pause to let Him love you.**

1. *Father, as you express yourself to me as the God who* _____
_____, *my heart is moved with*
_____.

2. *Father, as you express yourself to me as the God who* _____
_____, *my heart is moved with*
_____.

C. Jesus is available to love you like we read of His love in this chapter. Pause to express your heart to Him as you see Him in this chapter.

1. Describe how Jesus has loved you in some of the same ways that you read of His love in this chapter:

I have experienced the love of Jesus as He has _____
_____.

2. *Jesus, as you love me like you loved those in this chapter, my heart is touched with* _____.

DAY 3

P5

Ministering His life and love to our nearest ones at home and with family as well as faithful engagement in His body, the church

II. **Reflect on how you can better love your "near ones."** How might this text lead me to better love others? "As I have loved you, so you also should love one another." (John 13:34 NASB).

Since we have freely received of His love, we are to freely give this same love to others. Consider again how you see love portrayed in this chapter.

A. Who among your family or friends might you better love?

1. *I could better love_____,
   especially by _____.*

DAY 4

M1

Imparting the gospel and one's very life in daily activities and relationships, vocation and community

B. **Reflect on how you might be a witness of His love.** Notice again how Jesus expressed love by accepting, forgiving, or sacrificing? How might Jesus have taken initiative, expressed compassion, offered support, shared truth, and eternal hope?

1. Who in the traffic patterns of your life might benefit from receiving the blessing of Christ's love through you?
   (Who)_____could benefit from my sharing the love of Jesus by _____.

2. Who in your life could benefit from sharing part of your life story of encountering truth and eternal hope?
   *(Who)_____could benefit from my sharing more of
   _____.*

3. Pause now to pray for this person and then for yourself as you impart both your life and the gospel.

DAY 5

L4

Rejoicing regularly in my identity as "His Beloved"

III. **Reflect on *you* as the recipient of His love.** Your significance, value, and worth have been established by your Creator through the gift of His Son. How might this text affirm your identity as "His Beloved"?

"The light of God's love shined within us when he sent his matchless Son into the world so that we might live through him." (1 John 4:9).

Celebrate how you have received His love and grace, His forgiveness and new life, His calling and kingdom purpose.

A. Reread the text as His truth being shared just for you.

1. *I'm grateful that I have experienced the blessing of verse _____
   as I _____.*

B. Since He is the same yesterday, today, and forever, meditate on your being *in* the story of this chapter. Allow Him to love you as you read of His love in the chapter.

1. *My heart is touched with gratitude that Jesus _____
   _____.*

Walking in the Light of God's Son

Through Fresh Encounters With Jesus   John 12:35; John 8:12

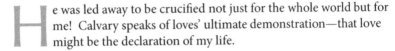

"Then Pilate handed Jesus over to them. So the soldiers seized him and took him away to be crucified" (John 19:16).

He was led away to be crucified not just for the whole world but for me! Calvary speaks of loves' ultimate demonstration—that love might be the declaration of my life.

"He was despised and rejected by men, a man of deep sorrows who was no stranger to suffering and grief" (Isaiah 53:3).

Pause and allow the Spirit to move your heart in loving response to Jesus.

■ What do you feel in your heart for Jesus? It's your ever-deepening love of Him that empowers your ever-widening love of others. "Deep" and "wide," such is His love!

As I consider the sorrowful Savior, despised and rejected "for me," my heart is moved with _____ for Him.

■ Now tell Jesus about what is in your heart. Respond to Him with compassion and love as you would for your most beloved friend.

Jesus, my heart is touched deeply with _____ as I consider your sacrifice for me. It grieves me deeply that _____ _____.

May my sadness for you in some mysterious way, bless you with my love. Might your Spirit prompt, in and through me to others, expressions of this same sacrificial love. In your name, amen."

SPIRIT
EMPOWERED
Faith

P9

Demonstrating His love to an ever-growing network of "others" as He continues to challenge us to love "beyond our comfort"

Walking in the Light of God's Word

Through Frequent Experience of Scripture   John 12:35; Psalm 119:105

"So when Jesus looked down and saw the disciple he loved standing with her, he said, 'Mother, look—John will be a son to you.' Then he said, 'John, look—she will be a mother to you!' From that day on, John accepted Mary into his home as one of his own family" (John 19:26–27).

P9

Demonstrating His love to an ever-growing network of "others" as He continues to challenge us to love "beyond our comfort"

From the cross, Jesus shares loving forgiveness to the soldiers. "Father forgive them…" From the cross, Jesus shares loving acceptance to the thief. "Today, I say you will be with me in paradise…" Now from the cross in His ever-widening demonstrations of love, Christ shares loving support toward His mother.

"Pour out all your worries and stress upon him and leave them there, for he always tenderly cares for you" (1 Peter 5:7).

Since Jesus is the same yesterday, today, and forever (Hebrews 13:8), consider a burden or need on your heart, and share it with Jesus.

I am reminded of this burden: _____.
(For example: I am reminded of the financial pressures I am facing. Or I am reminded of my daughter who is out of God's will).

■ Pause now and share your burden with Jesus. He still makes loving provision for those in need. Express your needs to the Lord and allow His Spirit to speak words of care and love to your heart.

Dear Jesus, I have this burden on my heart, and I need to be reassured that you care…

■ Imagine Christ sharing with you like He did with the soldiers, a thief, and His own mother: "I want to share in this hardship with you. I am here for you because I love you."

■ Now share with a partner or small group in prayers of yieldedness.

Holy Spirit, would you use my deepening love of Jesus to empower and prompt expressions of love to an ever-widening circle of my relationships.

Walking in the Light of God's People

Through Faithful Engagement in Fellowship   John 12:35; Matthew 5:14

"After this, Joseph from the city of Ramah, who was a secret disciple of Jesus for fear of the Jewish authorities, asked Pilate if he could remove the body of Jesus. So Pilate granted him permission to remove the body from the cross. Now Nicodemus, who had once come to Jesus privately at night, accompanied Joseph, and together they carried a significant amount of myrrh and aloes to the cross" (John 19:38–39).

Demonstrating His love to an ever-growing network of "others" as He continues to challenge us to love "beyond our comfort"

" **S** ecret disciple!" The two words do not go together. For me to be a disciple—a true follower—it will not be in secret. As I truly follow Him, He will lead me into ever-widening expressions of His love. No doubt, you have been the recipient of His sacrificial love shared through others, and as you gratefully embrace this love, you are freed to unselfishly love others. Both Joseph and Nicodemus seemed "slow to love" as secret disciples. Let's not be slow.

"Freely you received, freely give" (Matthew 10:8 NASB).

Recall a time when you were discouraged, misunderstood or "needy of love" in some way, but God brought another Jesus follower, family member, or friend to support and encourage you. How did this person reassure you, showing loving commitment to you so that you were not alone?

I remember a time when _____and God brought _____ into my life to _____.

Celebrate with a partner or small group. Talk about the times when God brought people in your life to encourage, support, and reassure you.

Celebrate these times with one another—acknowledging our great God and how He is at work to share His love through you and me as His people.

" We are ambassadors of the Anointed One who carry the message of Christ to the world, as though God were tenderly pleading with them…" (2 Corinthians 5:20).

How might you or your family or your Jesus community become ambassadors of Christ's love for one or more of the people in your life?

- Make a special snack and give it to a co-worker, neighbor, or family who is new to the workplace, neighborhood, or school.
- Involve your kids in sitting with someone at lunch who doesn't seem to have many friends.
- Organize a clothing drive, canned food drive, or "bring a penny" campaign for "the least of these" who are struggling financially
- Investigate where the "gates of hell" seem to be "winning" in your community—and prayerfully engage His church in sharing His love and the gospel (see Matthew 6:18).
- Ask the Holy Spirit to continue to widen His expression of His love and the gospel through you.

Pray with a partner or small group, asking the Holy Spirit to engage and empower you as an ambassador for Christ.

Demonstrating His love to an ever-growing network of "others" as He continues to challenge us to love "beyond our comfort"

John 20

REREAD JOHN 20 EACH DAY REFLECTING ON A DIFFERENT ASPECT OF HIS LOVE.

DAY 1

L3

Experiencing God as He really is through deepened intimacy with Him

I. **Reflect on how the REAL God is a God of love.** How might this text lead me to better love God? "We love because He first loved us" (1 John 4:19 NASB). We can only love the REAL God with all our "heart, soul, mind, and strength."

A. As you read and reflect on the chapter, how might you describe the REAL God as He is seen as Father, Son, and Holy Spirit?

1. In verse_____, He is seen as _____
   _____.

2. In verse _____, He is seen as _____
   _____.

3. In verse _____, the love of Jesus is seen toward_____
   as He _____.

4. In verse _____, the love of Jesus is seen toward_____
   as He _____.

5. How might these insights challenge some of your misconceptions of God?

   Sadly, I sometimes mistakenly see God as _____
   _____.

DAY 2

W1

Frequently being led by the Spirit into deeper love for the One who wrote the Word

B. **Reflect on how God has loved *you*** since He is the same yesterday, today, and forever (Hebrews 13:8). **Pause to let Him love you.**

1. *Father, as you express yourself to me as the God who* _____
   _____, *my heart is moved with*
   _____.

2. *Father, as you express yourself to me as the God who* _____
   _____, *my heart is moved with*
   _____.

C. Jesus is available to love you like we read of His love in this chapter. Pause to express your heart to Him as you see Him in this chapter.

1. Describe how Jesus has loved you in some of the same ways that you read of His love in this chapter:

   I have experienced the love of Jesus as He has _____
   _____.

2. *Jesus, as you love me like you loved those in this chapter, my heart is touched with* _____.

DAY 3

P5

Ministering His life and love to our nearest ones at home and with family as well as faithful engagement in His body, the church

II. **Reflect on how you can better love your "near ones."** How might this text lead me to better love others? "As I have loved you, so you also should love one another." (John 13:34 NASB).

Since we have freely received of His love, we are to freely give this same love to others. Consider again how you see love portrayed in this chapter.

A. Who among your family or friends might you better love?

1. *I could better love_____,*
   especially by _____.

DAY 4

M1

Imparting the gospel and one's very life in daily activities and relationships, vocation and community

B. **Reflect on how you might be a witness of His love.** Notice again how Jesus expressed love by accepting, forgiving, or sacrificing? How might Jesus have taken initiative, expressed compassion, offered support, shared truth, and eternal hope?

1. Who in the traffic patterns of your life might benefit from receiving the blessing of Christ's love through you?
   (Who)_____could benefit from my sharing the love of Jesus by _____.

2. Who in your life could benefit from sharing part of your life story of encountering truth and eternal hope?
   (Who)_____could benefit from my sharing more of
   _____.

3. Pause now to pray for this person and then for yourself as you impart both your life and the gospel.

DAY 5

L4

Rejoicing regularly in my identity as "His Beloved"

III. **Reflect on *you* as the recipient of His love.** Your significance, value, and worth have been established by your Creator through the gift of His Son. How might this text affirm your identity as "His Beloved"?

"The light of God's love shined within us when he sent his matchless Son into the world so that we might live through him." (1 John 4:9).

Celebrate how you have received His love and grace, His forgiveness and new life, His calling and kingdom purpose.

A. Reread the text as His truth being shared just for you.

1. *I'm grateful that I have experienced the blessing of verse _____*
   as I _____.

B. Since He is the same yesterday, today, and forever, meditate on your being *in* the story of this chapter. Allow Him to love you as you read of His love in the chapter.

1. *My heart is touched with gratitude that Jesus _____*
   _____.

Walking in the Light of God's Word

Through Frequent Experience of Scripture   John 12:35; Psalm 119:105

"For until then they hadn't understood the Scriptures that prophesied that he was destined to rise from the dead" (John 20:9).

M6

Bearing witness of a confident peace and expectant hope in God's Lordship in all things

For until then they hadn't understood the Scriptures that prophesied that he was destined to rise from the dead (John 20:9).

"…they did not yet know the Scripture" is an insightful message about where we find peace and hope. It seems that these disciples could have found benefit from personally embracing Christ's frequent words concerning His promised resurrection.

This same hope of embracing Scripture provides encouragement and security in our walk with Jesus. "The Scriptures impart to us encouragement and inspiration so that we can live in hope and endure all things" (Romans 15:4).

The Lord is "with us" as His Spirit brings direction and deepened relationship through His Word.

"May it be done to me according to your word" (Luke 1:38 NASB).

Join with one or two others, asking that His word becomes the explanation of your life.

Holy Spirit, I say 'Yes' to your God-breathed book. Without even knowing all that your word will ask of me, I yield for it to be true of me.

Walking in the Light of God's People

Through Faithful Engagement in Fellowship   John 12:35; Matthew 5:14

"Jesus repeated his greeting, 'Peace to you!' And he told them, 'Just as the Father has sent me, I'm now sending you'" (John 20:21).

To be "sent" with the heart and mission of Jesus is to live as a servant, sharing His life, love, and the gospel.

Recall a time when you were prompted to serve a friend, family member, or even a stranger during a time of need. "Freely you received, freely give" (Matthew 10:8). When did God involve you in ministry to another person at their point of need and aloneness?

I recall when (who/what) _____,
and God led me to _____.

(For example: I recall when several homeless people gathered near my house to stay warm. God prompted us to take them warm soup and blankets each day until the weather changed.)

Serving others with sensitivity and initiative is a critical part of our being "sent" to live and love as Jesus. Christ exemplified this when He noticed the many needs of hurting people around Him and took initiative to meet those needs.

Take notice of opportunities to be "sent" as a servant to others in your life.

- Look for the *unnoticed* people around you. Start a conversation. Ask them about the details of their lives.

- Offer to help someone with their groceries, offer your seat on the bus, or even buy a cup of coffee for the person next in line.

- Take care packages to the homeless in your town or volunteer to deliver meals to the elderly.

Follow Jesus' example. Pray with others to live out this request:

Heavenly Father, I want to be a better servant to my family, coworkers, neighbors, friends, and others around me. Help me this week to lift my focus beyond myself to notice the needs of others. Holy Spirit, prompt my mind and empower my initiative to meet these needs.

SPIRIT EMPOWERED
Faith
L3

Experiencing God as He really is through deepened intimacy with Him

Walking in the Light of God's Son

Through Fresh Encounters With Jesus   John 12:35; John 8:12

"But all that is recorded here is so that you will fully believe that Jesus is the Anointed One, the Son of God, and that through your faith in him you will experience eternal life by the power of his name" (John 20:31).

M6

Bearing witness of a confident peace and expectant hope in God's Lordship in all things

Notice the patience and pursuing grace we find in Jesus' love of Mary, the disciples, and a hesitant Thomas. We also have received this same loving pursuit as it provides hopeful confidence of His Lordship.

"And even more than that, we overflow with triumphant joy in our new relationship of living in harmony with God—all because of Jesus Christ!" (Romans 5:11).

Let's be reminded that before we were drawn into a personal relationship with God, we were separated from Him. Because of our sin, we had no friendship, no relationship, and no peace with God. Because of His grace, we were saved from our eternal separation from God. We were reconciled, brought back, and restored in our relationship with Him.

Pause quietly before the Lord as He reminds you what life would have been without Him? Ask Him to remind you of His grace and how the Lord brought you back, made things right, and restored you.

I'm especially glad that God brought me to Him because _____
_____.

I rejoice in God's grace because without Him, I would _____
_____.

Now, with a partner or small group, "rejoice" together in your having received reconciliation. The Lord smiles when He sees His people living out His Book—experiencing the Scriptures—and in this we find peace and confident hope.

Experiencing God as
He really is through
deepened intimacy with
Him

> **LOVE THE LORD YOUR GOD WITH ALL YOUR HEART, SOUL AND MIND**
> …and love your neighbor as you love yourself. The whole law and the prophets depend on these two commandments" (Matthew 22:37–40 NASB).

REREAD JOHN 21 EACH DAY REFLECTING ON A DIFFERENT ASPECT OF HIS LOVE.

DAY 1

L3

Experiencing God as He really is through deepened intimacy with Him

I. **Reflect on how the REAL God is a God of love.** How might this text lead me to better love God? "We love because He first loved us" (1 John 4:19 NASB). We can only love the REAL God with all our "heart, soul, mind, and strength."

A. As you read and reflect on the chapter, how might you describe the REAL God as He is seen as Father, Son, and Holy Spirit?

1. In verse _____, He is seen as _____
_____.

2. In verse _____, He is seen as _____
_____.

3. In verse _____, the love of Jesus is seen toward_____
as He _____.

4. In verse _____, the love of Jesus is seen toward_____
as He _____.

5. How might these insights challenge some of your misconceptions of God?

Sadly, I sometimes mistakenly see God as _____
_____.

DAY 2

W1

Frequently being led by the Spirit into deeper love for the One who wrote the Word

B. **Reflect on how God has loved *you*** since He is the same yesterday, today, and forever (Hebrews 13:8). **Pause to let Him love you.**

1. *Father, as you express yourself to me as the God who* _____
_____, *my heart is moved with*
_____.

2. *Father, as you express yourself to me as the God who* _____
_____, *my heart is moved with*
_____.

C. Jesus is available to love you like we read of His love in this chapter. Pause to express your heart to Him as you see Him in this chapter.

1. Describe how Jesus has loved you in some of the same ways that you read of His love in this chapter:

I have experienced the love of Jesus as He has _____
_____.

2. *Jesus, as you love me like you loved those in this chapter, my heart is touched with* _____.

DAY 3

P5

Ministering His life and love to our nearest ones at home and with family as well as faithful engagement in His body, the church

II. **Reflect on how you can better love your "near ones."** How might this text lead me to better love others? "As I have loved you, so you also should love one another." (John 13:34 NASB).

Since we have freely received of His love, we are to freely give this same love to others. Consider again how you see love portrayed in this chapter.

A. Who among your family or friends might you better love?

1. *I could better love_____,*
   especially by _____.

DAY 4

M1

Imparting the gospel and one's very life in daily activities and relationships, vocation and community

B. **Reflect on how you might be a witness of His love.** Notice again how Jesus expressed love by accepting, forgiving, or sacrificing? How might Jesus have taken initiative, expressed compassion, offered support, shared truth, and eternal hope?

1. Who in the traffic patterns of your life might benefit from receiving the blessing of Christ's love through you?
   (Who)_____could benefit from my sharing the love of Jesus by _____.

2. Who in your life could benefit from sharing part of your life story of encountering truth and eternal hope?
   (Who)_____could benefit from my sharing more of
   _____.

3. Pause now to pray for this person and then for yourself as you impart both your life and the gospel.

DAY 5

L4

Rejoicing regularly in my identity as "His Beloved"

III. **Reflect on *you* as the recipient of His love.** Your significance, value, and worth have been established by your Creator through the gift of His Son. How might this text affirm your identity as "His Beloved"?

"The light of God's love shined within us when he sent his matchless Son into the world so that we might live through him." (1 John 4:9).

Celebrate how you have received His love and grace, His forgiveness and new life, His calling and kingdom purpose.

A. Reread the text as His truth being shared just for you.

1. *I'm grateful that I have experienced the blessing of verse _____*
   as I _____.

B. Since He is the same yesterday, today, and forever, meditate on your being *in* the story of this chapter. Allow Him to love you as you read of His love in the chapter.

1. *My heart is touched with gratitude that Jesus _____*
   _____.

Walking in the Light of God's Son

Through Fresh Encounters With Jesus   John 12:35; John 8:12

"This was the third time Jesus appeared to his disciples after his resurrection" (John 21:14).

Jesus is still making Himself known today! He may not be revealing Himself with nets full of fish, but His presence and witness are clearly being made known.

He can reveal Himself through Scripture, or He can reveal Himself through a testimony, the beauty of a summer day, or even in still and quiet moments. Think about the moment when you surrendered to Jesus Christ. How did God reveal Jesus to you? Was it through the example of a family member or a friend? Was it in a sermon or through the Scriptures? Was it through a testimony? Did He meet you and reveal Himself directly? How did you "hear" Him and come to know Him?

God revealed Jesus to me through _____.

My yielding to Christ involved _____.

Championing Jesus as the only hope of eternal life and abundant living

Pause quietly to give Him thanks.

Lord Jesus, receive the gladness of my heart as an expression of my love.

The disciples yielded to Christ's words to "throw your nets over the starboard side" (John 21:6), and similarly this is the role of each Christ follower. Christ "reveals," and His followers are to "yield."

Now with a partner or small group, reflect on your own yielding to the revelation of Jesus.

Holy Spirit, prompt and empower my walk of yieldedness.

Walking in the Light of God's Word
Through Frequent Experience of Scripture   John 12:35; Psalm 119:105

"And then he said,
'Peter, follow me.'"
(John 21:19)

Two powerful, simple words that change everything: "Follow Me."
To follow Him is to avoid a *broad road* that many travel leading to
destruction; choosing instead a *narrow road* leading to life
(Matthew 7:13–14).

Consider the blessing that Christ has invited you to follow Him, to "partner"
with Him in kingdom purposes.

Pause to consider that God's ultimate purpose for your life is to follow Him
so that you can express His glory, which…

- Allows you to receive of God's abundant blessings.

- Enables you to bless others with His love.

- Blesses God and brings Him pleasure.

SPIRIT
EMPOWERED
Faith

M3

Championing Jesus as
the only hope of eternal
life and abundant living

What do these truths do to your heart? Might you be touched to offer a
sacrifice of thanksgiving to God, confident that such an offering honors and
glorifies Him?

"He who offers a sacrifice of thanksgiving honors Me" (Psalm 50:23).

Share with Him your response to the following:

*Jesus, as I consider the wonder that my "following" you actually blesses you
and others around me, my heart is filled with* _____
_____.

(For example: My heart is filled with praise, awe, wonder, gratitude, love, joy.
I cannot fully comprehend how much you love me, and I hope I never do!)

Pause to pray with your partner or small group, giving God honor
through your praise and thanksgiving that He's inviting you to follow, and
you have the privilege of joining Him in an eternal calling.

*Lord Jesus, from a grateful heart, lead me by your Spirit as I champion you as
people's only hope.*

Walking in the Light of God's People

Through Faithful Engagement in Fellowship   John 12:35; Matthew 5:14

"I, John, am that disciple who has written these things to testify of the truth, and we know that what I've documented is accurate" (John 21:24).

M3

Championing Jesus as the only hope of eternal life and abundant living

The apostle John "knows" this gospel story is true because he was there for the teaching and miracles, the crucifixion, empty tomb, and confirming appearances!

Pause with a partner or small group to consider the impact of the "truth" that John experienced.

Imagine Jesus' agony on the cross. He was prepared to take upon Himself the sins of the world. Jesus sensed that His own Father had turned His back on Him. He cried out with a voice that conveyed a feeling of utter abandonment: "My God, my God, why have you forsaken me? (Mark 15:34 NASB). Yet there He hung upon a cross, startling people with His love. He was dying, yet He was thinking of those around Him—the soldier, the thief, His mother. Jesus was giving His life, yet He was giving life to others so that they might know His love.

That is the startling love of Christ. We can share in His love and then share God's love with others.

For whom did Christ do all of this? For whom did He suffer and die? Listen as the Spirit whispers, "He did it for you!" If He did not need to die for anyone else, He would have done it just for you! Allow this wondrous truth to motivate you to share with others the hope of His love.

Now would you join in receiving His startling love through a bold declaration of faith: *"He did it for me."* Whisper it again. *"He did it for me."*

Let's pause, be still, and give Him thanks for the startling love of Jesus and the privilege of making Him known to others:

Holy Spirit, fill me with your constraining love and with a grateful heart.
I yield to be a faithful witness of Jesus whom I also have experienced as true.

Championing Jesus as
the only hope of eternal
life and abundant living

"From here on,
   worshiping the Father
will not be a matter of the right place
      but with the right heart.
   For God is a Spirit,
and he longs to have sincere worshipers
      who worship and adore him
in the realm of the Spirit and in truth."

—John 4:23

About the Great Commandment Network

The Great Commandment Network is an international collaborative network of strategic kingdom leaders from the faith community, marketplace, education, and caregiving fields who prioritize the powerful simplicity of the words of Jesus to love God, love others, and see others become His followers (Matthew 22:37–40; 19–20).

The Great Commandment Network is served through these entities.

Relationship Press

This team collaborates, supports, and joins together with churches, denominational partners, and professional associates to develop, print, and produce resources that facilitate ongoing Great Commandment ministry.

The Center for Relational Leadership

Their mission is to teach, train, and mentor both ministry and corporate leaders in Great Commandment principles, seeking to equip leaders with relational skills, so they might lead as Jesus led.

The Galatians 6:6 Retreat Ministry

This ministry offers a unique two-day retreat for ministers and their spouses for personal renewal and for reestablishing and affirming ministry and family priorities.

The Center for Relational Care (CRC)

The CRC provides therapy and support to relationships in crisis through an accelerated process of growth and healing, including Relational Care Intensives for couples, families, and singles.

For more information on how you, your church, ministry, denomination, or movement can be served by the Great Commandment Network write or call:

> Great Commandment Network
> 2511 South Lakeline Blvd.
> Cedar Park, Texas 78613
> Phone: 800.881.8008

> Visit our website at www.GreatCommandment.net

Introduction to Outcomes

A Spirit-empowered Faith Expresses Itself in Great Commission Living Empowered by Great Commandment Love

---

A Spirit-empowered faith begins with the end in mind.
The Great Commission calls us to make disciples.

"Now go in my authority and make disciples of all nations, baptizing them in the name of the Father, the Son, and the Holy Spirit. 20 And teach them to faithfully follow[a] all that I have commanded you. And never forget that I am with you every day, even to the completion of this age" (Matthew 28:19–20).

The ultimate goal of our faith journey is to relate to the person of Jesus because it is our relational connection to Jesus that will produce Christ-likeness and spiritual growth. This relational perspective of discipleship is required if we hope to have a faith that is marked by the Spirit's power.

Models of discipleship that are based solely upon what we know and what we do are incomplete, lacking the empowerment of a life of loving and living intimately with Jesus. **A Spirit-empowered faith is relational and impossible to realize apart from a special work of the Spirit.** For example, the Spirit-empowered outcome of "listening to and hearing God" implies relationship. It is both relational in focus and requires the Holy Spirit's power to live.

A Spirit-empowered faith begins at the right place. The Great Commandment calls us to start with loving God and loving others.

"You must 'love the Lord your God with all your heart, all your soul, and all your mind.' This is the first and greatest commandment. A second is equally important: 'Love your neighbor as yourself.' The entire law and all the demands of the prophets are based on these two commandments" (Matthew 22:37–40 NLT).

Relevant discipleship does not begin with doctrines or teaching, parables or stewardship, but with loving the Lord with all your heart, mind, soul, and strength and then loving the people closest to you. Since Matthew 22:37–40 gives us the first and greatest commandment, **a Spirit-empowered faith starts where the Great Commandment tells us to start. A disciple must first learn to deeply love the Lord and to express His love to the "nearest ones"**—his family, church, and community (and in that order).

A Spirit-empowered faith embraces a relational process of Christ-likeness.

Scripture reminds us that there are three sources of light for our journey—Jesus, His Word, and His people. The process of discipleship (or becoming more like Jesus) occurs as we relate intimately with each source of light.

"...walk in the light, so the darkness will not overtake you| (John 12:35).

Spirit-empowered discipleship will require a lifestyle that incorporates the following:

- Fresh encounters with Jesus (John 8:12)

- Frequent experiences of Scripture (Psalm 119:105)

- Faithful engagement with God's people (Matthew 5:14)

A Spirit-empowered faith can be defined with observable outcomes using a biblical framework.

The metrics for measuring Spirit-empowered faith or the growth of a disciple come from Scripture and are organized/framed around four distinct dimensions of a disciple who serves.

Now these are the ministries Christ gave to the church: the apostles, the prophets, the evangelists, and the pastors and teachers. Their responsibility is to equip God's people to do His work and build up the church, the body of Christ (Ephesians 4:11–12 NLT).

A relational framework for organizing Spirit-empowered discipleship outcomes draws from a cluster analysis of several Greek (*diakoneo, leitourgeo, douleuo*) and Hebrew (*'abad, sharath*) words, which elaborate on the Ephesians 4:12 declaration that Christ's followers are to be equipped for works of ministry or service. Therefore, the 40 Spirit-empowered faith outcomes have been identified and organized around:

- **Serving/loving the Lord**—"While they were **ministering** to the Lord and fasting…" (Acts 13:2 NASB).[1]

- **Serving/loving the Word**—"But we will devote ourselves to prayer and to the **ministry** of the word" (Acts 6:4 NASB).[2]

- **Serving/loving people**—"Through love **serve** one another" (Galatians 5:13 NASB).[3]

- **Serving/living His mission**—"Now all these things are from God, who reconciled us to Himself through Christ and gave us the **ministry** of reconciliation" (2 Corinthians 5:18 NASB).[4]

---

[1] Ferguson, David L. *Great Commandment Principle.* Cedar Park, Texas: Relationship Press, 2013).

[2] Ferguson, David L. *Relational Foundations.* Cedar Park, Texas: Relationship Press, 2004.

[3] Ferguson, David L. *Relational Discipleship.* Cedar Park, Texas: Relationship Press, 2005.

[4] "Spirit-Empowered Outcomes", Empowered 21 Global Council, Online: http://empowered21.com/discipleship-materials/.

A Spirit-empowered Disciple LOVES THE LORD through

L1. Practicing thanksgiving in all things
"Enter the gates with thanksgiving" (Ps. 100:4). "In everything give thanks" (1 Thess. 5:18). "As sorrowful, yet always rejoicing" (2 Cor. 6:10).

L2. Listening to and hearing God for direction and discernment
"Speak Lord, Your servant is listening" (1 Sam. 3:8–9). "Mary…listening to the Lord's word, seated at his feet" (Luke10:38–42). "Shall I not share with Abraham what I am about to do?" (Gen. 18:17). "His anointing teaches you all things" (1 John 2:27).

L3. Experiencing God as He really is through deepened intimacy with Him
"Hear, O Israel: The Lord our God, the Lord is one. Love the Lord your God with all your heart and with all your soul and with all your strength" (Deut. 6:4–5). "Yet the Lord longs to be gracious to you; therefore he will rise up to show you compassion. For the Lord is a God of justice" (Isa. 30:18). See also John 14:9.

L4. Rejoicing regularly in my identity as "His Beloved"
"And His banner over me is love" (Song 2:4). "To the praise of the glory of His grace, which He freely bestowed on us in the beloved" (Eph. 1:6). "For the Lord gives to His beloved even in their sleep" (Ps. 127:2).

L5. Living with a passionate longing for purity and to please Him in all things
"Who may ascend the hill of the Lord—he who has clean hands and a pure heart" (Ps. 24:3). "Beloved, let us cleanse ourselves from all of flesh and spirit, perfecting holiness in the fear of God" (2 Cor. 7:1). "I always do the things that are pleasing to Him" (John 8:29). "Though He slay me, yet will I hope in Him" (Job 13:15).

L6. Consistent practice of self-denial, fasting, and solitude rest
"He turned and said to Peter, 'Get behind me, Satan! You are an obstacle to me. You are thinking not as God does, but as human beings do'" (Matt. 16:23). "But you when you fast…" (Matt. 6:17). "Be still and know that I am God" (Ps. 46:10).

L7. Entering often into Spirit-led praise and worship
"Bless the Lord O my soul and all that is within me…" (Ps. 103:1). "Worship the Lord with reverence" (Ps. 2:11). "I praise Thee O Father, Lord of heaven and earth…" (Matt. 11:25).

L8. Disciplined, bold, and believing prayer
"Pray at all times in the Spirit" (Eph. 6:18). "Call unto me and I will answer…" (Jer. 33:3). "If you ask according to His will—He hears—and you will have…" (1 John 5:14–15).

L9. Yielding to the Spirit's fullness as life in the Spirit brings supernatural intimacy with the Lord, manifestation of divine gifts, and witness of the fruit of the Spirit
"For by one Spirit we were all baptized into one body, whether Jews or Greeks, whether slaves or free, and we were all made to drink of one Spirit" (1 Cor. 12:13). "You shall receive power when the Holy Spirit comes upon you" (Acts 1:8). "But to each one is given the manifestation of the Spirit for the common good" (1 Cor. 12:7). See also, 1 Peter 4:10, and Rom. 12:6.

L10. Practicing the presence of the Lord, yielding to the Spirit's work of Christ-likeness
"And we who with unveiled faces all reflect the Lord's glory, are being transformed into His likeness from glory to glory which comes from the Lord, who is the Spirit" (2 Cor. 3:18). "As the deer pants after the water brooks, so my soul pants after You, O God" (Ps. 42:1).

A Spirit-empowered Disciple LIVES THE WORD through

W1. Frequently being led by the Spirit into deeper love for the One who wrote the Word
"Love the Lord thy God—love thy neighbor; upon these two commandments deepens all the law and prophets" (Matt. 22:37–40). "I delight in Your commands because I love them." (Ps. 119:47). "The ordinances of the Lord are pure—they are more precious than gold—sweeter than honey" (Ps. 19:9–10).

W2. Being a "living epistle" in reverence and awe as His Word becomes real in my life, vocation, and calling
"You yourselves are our letter—known and read by all men" (2 Cor. 3:2). "And the Word became flesh and dwelt among us" (John 1:14). "Husbands love your wives—cleansing her by the washing with water through the Word" (Eph. 5:26). See also Titus 2:5. "Whatever you do, do your work heartily, as for the Lord…" (Col. 3:23).

W3. Yielding to the Scripture's protective cautions and transforming power to bring life change in me
"I gain understanding from Your precepts; therefore I hate every wrong path" (Ps. 119:104). "Be it done unto me according to Your word" (Luke 1:38). "How can a young man keep his way pure? By living according to Your word" (Ps. 119:9). See also Col. 3:16–17.

W4. Humbly and vulnerably sharing of the Spirit's transforming work through the Word
"I will speak of your statutes before kings and will not be put to shame" (Ps. 119:46). "Preach the word; be ready in season and out of season" (2 Tim. 4:2).

W5. Meditating consistently on more and more of the Word hidden in the heart
"I have hidden Your Word in my heart that I might not sin against You" (Ps. 119:12). "May the words of my mouth and the meditation of my heart be pleasing in Your sight, O Lord, my rock and my redeemer" (Ps. 19:14).

W6. Encountering Jesus in the Word for deepened transformation in Christ-likeness
"All of us, gazing with unveiled face on the glory of the Lord, are being transformed into the same image from glory to glory, as from the Lord who is the Spirit" (2 Cor. 3:18). "If you abide in Me and My words abide in you, ask whatever you wish, and it will be done for you" (John 15:7). See also Luke 24:32, Ps. 119:136, and 2 Cor. 1:20.

W7. A life explained as one of "experiencing Scripture"
"This is that spoken of by the prophets" (Acts 2:16). "My comfort in my suffering is this: Your promise preserves my life" (Ps. 119:50). "My soul is consumed with longing for Your laws at all times" (Ps. 119:20).

W8. Living "naturally supernatural," in all of life, as His Spirit makes the written Word *(logos)* the living Word *(Rhema)*
"Faith comes by hearing and hearing by the Word (Rhema) of Christ" (Rom. 10:17). "Your Word is a lamp to my feet and a light for my path" (Ps. 119:105).

W9. Living abundantly "in the present" as His Word brings healing to hurt, anger, guilt, fear, and condemnation—which are *heart hindrances* to life abundant
"The thief comes to steal, kill and destroy…" (John 10:10). "I run in the path of Your commands for You have set my heart free" (Ps. 119:32). "…and you shall know the truth and the truth shall set you free" (John 8:32). "For freedom Christ set us free; so stand firm and do not submit again to the yoke of slavery" (Gal. 5:1).

W10. Implicit, unwavering trust that His Word will never fail
"The grass withers and the flower fades but the Word of God abides forever" (Isa. 40:8). "So will My word be which goes forth from My mouth, it will not return to me empty" (Isa. 55:11).

A Spirit-empowered Disciple LOVES PEOPLE through

P1. Living a Spirit-led life of doing good in all of life—relationships and vocation, community and calling
"…He went about doing good…" (Acts 10:38). "Let your light shine before men in such a way that they may see your good works, and glorify your Father who is in heaven" (Matt. 5:16). "But love your enemies, and do good, and lend, expecting nothing in return, and your reward will be great, and you will be sons of the Most High; for He Himself is kind to ungrateful and evil men" (Luke 6:35). See also Rom. 15:2.

P2. Startling people with loving initiatives to give first
"Give, and it will be given to you. They will pour into your lap a good measure—pressed down, shaken together, and running over. For by your standard of measure it will be measured to you in return" (Luke 6:38). "But Jesus was saying, 'Father, forgive them; for they do not know what they are doing." (Luke 23:34). See also Luke 23:43 and John 19:27.

P3. Discerning the relational needs of others with a heart to give of His love
"Let no unwholesome word proceed from your mouth, but only such a word as is good for edification according to the need of the moment, so that it will give grace to those who hear" (Eph. 4:29). "And my God will supply all your needs according to His riches in glory in Christ Jesus" (Phil. 4:19). See also Luke 6:30.

P4. Seeing people as needing BOTH redemption from sin AND intimacy in relationships, addressing both human fallenness and aloneness
"But God demonstrates His own love toward us, in that while we were yet sinners, Christ died for us" (Rom. 5:8). "When Jesus came to the place, He looked up and said to him, 'Zaccheus, hurry and come down, for today I must stay at your house'" (Luke 19:5). See also Mark 8:24 and Gen. 2:18.

P5. Ministering His life and love to our *nearest ones* at home and with family as well as faithful engagement in His body, the church
"You husbands in the same way, live with your wives in an understanding way, as with someone weaker, since she is a woman; and show her honor as a fellow heir of the grace of life, so that your prayers will not be hindered" (1 Peter 3:7). See also 1 Peter 3:1 and Ps. 127:3.

P6. Expressing the fruit of the Spirit as a lifestyle and identity
"But the fruit of the Spirit is love, joy, peace, patience, kindness, goodness, faithfulness, gentleness, self-control…" (Gal. 5:22–23). "With the fruit of a man's mouth his stomach will be satisfied; He will be satisfied with the product of his lips" (Prov. 18:20).

P7. Expecting and demonstrating the supernatural as His spiritual gifts are made manifest and His grace is at work by His Spirit
*"In the power of signs and wonders, in the power of the **Spirit**; so that from Jerusalem and round about as far as Illyricum I have fully preached the gospel of Christ" (Rom. 15:19). "Truly, truly, I say to you, he who believes in Me, the works that I do, he will do also…"(John 14:12). See also 1 Cor. 14:1.*

P8. Taking courageous initiative as a peacemaker, reconciling relationships along life's journey
"…Live in peace with one another" (1 Thess. 5:13). "For He Himself is our peace, who made both groups into one and broke down the barrier of the dividing wall" (Eph. 2:14). "Therefore, confess your sins to one another, and pray for one another so that you may be healed. See also James 5:16 and Eph. 4:31–32.

P9. Demonstrating His love to an ever-growing network of "others" as He continues to challenge us to love "beyond our comfort"
"The one who says, 'I have come to know Him,' and does not keep His commandments, is a liar, and the truth is not in him" (1 John 2:4). "If someone says, 'I love God,' and hates his brother, he is a liar; for the one who does not love his brother whom he has seen, cannot love God whom he has not seen" (1 John 4:20).

P10. Humbly acknowledging to the Lord, ourselves, and others that it is Jesus in and through us who is loving others at their point of need
"Take My yoke upon you and learn from Me, for I am gentle and humble in heart, and you will find rest for your souls" (Matt. 11:29). "If I then, the Lord and the Teacher, washed your feet, you also ought to wash one another's feet" (John 13:14).

A Spirit-empowered Disciple LIVES HIS MISSION through

M1. Imparting the gospel and one's very life in daily activities and relationships, vocation, and community
"Having so fond an affection for you, we were well-pleased to impart to you not only the gospel of God but also our own lives, because you had become very dear to us" (1 Thess. 2:8–9). See also Eph. 6:19.

M2. Expressing and extending the kingdom of God as compassion, justice, love, and forgiveness are shared
"I must preach the kingdom of God to the other cities also, for I was sent for this purpose'" (Luke 4:43). "As You sent Me into the world, I also have sent them into the world"(John 17:18). "Restore to me the joy of Your salvation and sustain me with a willing spirit. Then I will teach transgressors Your ways, and sinners will be converted to you"(Ps. 51:12–13). See also Mic. 6:8.

M3. Championing Jesus as the only hope of eternal life and abundant living
"There is no salvation through anyone else, nor is there any other name under heaven given to the human race by which we are to be saved" (Acts 4:12). "A thief comes only to steal and slaughter and destroy; I came so that they might have life and have it more abundantly" (John 10:10). See also Acts 4:12, John 10:10, and John 14:6.

M4. Yielding to the Spirit's role to convict others as He chooses, resisting expressions of condemnation
"And He, when He comes, will convict the world concerning sin and righteousness and judgment…"(John 16:8). "Who is the one who condemns? Christ Jesus is He who died, yes, rather who was raised, who is at the right hand of God, who also intercedes for us" (Rom. 8:34). See also Rom. 8:1.

M5. Ministering His life and love to the "least of these"
"Then He will answer them, 'Truly I say to you, to the extent that you did not do it to one of the least of these, you did not do it to Me'" (Matt. 25:45). "Pure and undefiled religion in the sight of our God and Father is this: to visit orphans and widows in their distress, and to keep oneself unstained by the world" (James 1:27).

M6. Bearing witness of a confident peace and expectant hope in God's Lordship in all things
"Now may the Lord of peace Himself continually grant you peace in every circumstance. The Lord be with you all!" (2 Thess. 3:16). "Let the peace of Christ rule in your hearts, to which indeed you were called in one body; and be thankful" (Col. 3:15). See also Rom. 8:28 and Ps. 146:5.

M7. Faithfully sharing of time, talent, gifts, and resources in furthering His mission
"Of this church I was made a minister according to the stewardship from God bestowed on me for your benefit, so that I might fully carry out the preaching of the word of God" (Col. 1:25). "From everyone who has been given much, much will be required; and to whom they entrusted much, of him they will ask all the more" (Luke 12:48). See also 1 Cor. 4:1–2.

M8. Attentive listening to others' *story*, vulnerably sharing of your story, and a sensitive witness of Jesus' story as life's ultimate hope; developing your story of prodigal, preoccupied and pain-filled living; listening for others' story and sharing Jesus' story
"…but sanctify Christ as Lord in your hearts, always being ready to make a defense to everyone who asks you to give an account for the hope that is in you, yet with gentleness and reverence" (1 Peter 3:15). "…because this son of mine was dead, and has come to life again" (Luke 11:24). (Mark 5:21–42). (John 9:1–35).

M9. Pouring our life into others, making disciples who in turn make disciples of others
"Go therefore and make disciples of all nations, baptizing them in the name of the Father and the Son and the Holy Spirit, teaching them to observe all that I commanded you; and lo, I am with you always, even to the end of the age" (Matt. 28:19–20). See also 2 Tim. 2:2.

M10. Living submissively within His body, the church, as instruction and encouragement, reproof, and correction are graciously received by faithful disciples
"…and be subject to one another in the fear of Christ" (Eph. 5:21). "Brethren, even if anyone is caught in any trespass, you who are spiritual, restore such a one in a spirit of gentleness; each one looking to yourself, so that you too will not be tempted" (Gal. 6:1). See also Gal. 6:2.

An Age-Stage Model for Spirit-Empowered Disciples

First-century faith followed a pattern of Belong–Become–Believe!

- "Come follow me" Matthew 4:19 (Belong)
- "Lord, teach us to pray" Luke 11:1 (Become)
- "You are the Christ" Matthew 16:16 (Believe)

CAUTION!

Numerous studies, including the Willowcreek *Reveal* study, indicate that the process below, in many ways, has broken down between stages 2 and 3 (i.e. what we have *explored* and personally *embraced* has *not become an experienced lifestyle* and thus not the believer's identity).

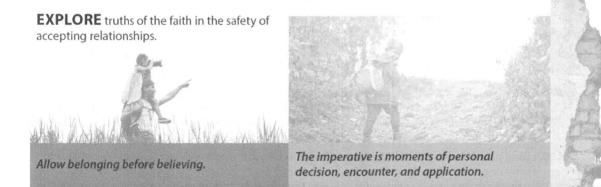

EXPLORE truths of the faith in the safety of accepting relationships.

EMBRACE truths of the faith in a personal way.

Allow belonging before believing.

The imperative is moments of personal decision, encounter, and application.

➤ *Process of Faith Formation Requires Encounters with. . .*

Belong-Become-Believe

The Willowcreek *Reveal* study uses the four terms, Exploring Christ, Growing in Christ, Close to Christ, and Christ-Centered.

Early church followers used stage terms such as seeker, hearer, kneeler, faithful.

The Apostolic Tradition written around A.D. 215 by Hippolytus, bishop of Rome, is documented by Robert E. Webber in *Journey to Jesus* (Abington Press, 2001), pages 11–15.

EXPERIENCE truths of the faith in everyday life.

EXPRESS truths of the faith to others through your identity as a Christ-follower.

Selected Outcomes:
A Spirit-Empowered Disciple:
- Listens to and hears God.
- Lives life through experiencing Scripture.
- Shares His love with near ones beginning at home.
- Yields to the Spirit for intimacy and discernment, direction and empowerment.

CAUTION! Monday–Friday living is where discipleship too often breaks down.

Identity is contagious as others follow this Explore–Embrace–Experience–Express process.

Jesus, Experiences of Scripture and Engaging Community ⟶

 **great commandment network**

The Great Commandment Network offers additional resources designed to support personal growth, relationship growth and Spirit-empowered discipleship.

Available at greatcommandment.net/resources

SPIRIT-EMPOWERED FAITH

What Bible verses have you actually experienced recently?

The first century church turned the world upside down for Christ because they had two simple, but powerful, commandments as their guide: love God and love people (Matthew 22:37–40).

How is it possible that the twenty-first century church, with all its available resources, seems to barely survive?

- Could it be that we've lost the powerful simplicity of love?

- Could it be that we've lost the first century church's emphasis on a *relational* faith?

- Could it be that we've lost the priority of making disciples who make disciples?

The Experiential Gospel of John Kit

The Experiential Gospel of John is designed to engage followers of Jesus as they seek to impart the gospel and live out a relevant, daily faith. Take a journey though the Gospel of John with this resource and encounter the heart of the Savior in a new way.

The kit includes:

- 8 copies of *The Experiential Gospel of John*

- 8 copies of *The Story of Jesus,* The Passion Translation

- The Spirit-Empowered Faith set: A brochure explaining the Spirit-empowered Faith content; 40 outcomes of a Spirit-empowered disciple of Jesus; Self-assessment tool to measure the 40 outcomes in your own life and those in your small group; 12-part teaching notes on the Spirit-empowered Faith that can be used as sermon guides or leader notes

The Experiential Gospel of John: A Guided Discipleship Journey in a Spirit-empowered Faith

This resource is unique because the exercises in each chapter were written with the specific goal of engaging you in a Spirit-empowered faith. Why is that important? Because it is only an experiential, Spirit-empowered faith that can change our lives and the lives of those around us.

Each chapter of this resource will engage you to move beyond simply seeking to know or study God's truth, to actually *experiencing* it through:

- A daily, guided reading plan that emphasizes how Scripture has BOTH objective meaning and relational significance as you actually DO Bible verses.

- A guided plan for spiritual growth based upon 40 discipleship outcomes which are RELATIONAL and impossible to live apart from the Holy Spirit!

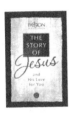

The Story of Jesus and His Love for You

Experience the life and love of Jesus as told in this pocket-sized gospel of John, The Passion Translation. This new, heart-level translation expresses God's fiery heart of love to this generation using Hebrew, Greek, and Aramaic manuscripts, merging the emotion and life-changing truth of God's Word.

Spirit-empowered Faith Reports

Track your personal or church's discipleship journey from EXPLORING 40 critical outcomes, to personally EMBRACING them, to EXPERIENCING them in daily life, and then into maturity as these outcomes are EXPRESSED as your IDENTITY!

Individual Report

This 39-page report provides a graphic display of strengths and growth areas across 40 Spirit-empowered Faith Discipleship Outcomes displaying a snapshot of how *you* are doing in loving the Lord, living His Word, loving people, and living His mission. Learn about recommended resources and strategies for engaging STRENGTHS in discipling others, plus *experiential* devotions targeted for each GROWTH area.

Group Report

This 140-page report compiles the anonymous results of a group of Individual Reports with a graphic summary. It also details STRENGTHS and GROWTH AREAS. Plus, it provides teaching/preaching outlines and experiential devotions, all built around the 40 Spirit-empowered Faith Outcomes.

MARRIAGE

Intimate Encounters

Through *Intimate Encounters*, participants will learn how to identify relationship needs such as attention, affection, and respect; learn to emotionally care for one another; strengthen oneness in spirit, soul, and body; resolve painful emotions such as hurt, anger, guilt, and communicate honestly and lovingly. Experience the marriage you've always wanted!

PARENTING

Parenting with Intimacy

How can you discover what your children need most?

This resource provides practical, Christ-centered principles for truly knowing your children, allowing them to know you, and hands-on exercises to become caringly involved in their lives. It is a great workbook for engaging parents in a Deuteronomy 6 vision for discipling their own children.

Extreme Home Makeover

This resource focuses on renovating relationships and imparting faith at home. Parents, live out your calling to disciple your children, engage others around you with Biblical principles that work. Learn how to experience truth and live in community. This resource is great for anyone—couples, singles, and youth! There is something for everyone.

RELATIONAL HEALTH

Top Ten Relational Needs Workshop

Top Ten Relational Needs is a course of study designed to help participants explore key relational needs that all humans share. This resource will help participants gain greater insight into the ways that God meets their relational needs, as well as equip them to better recognize and meet the needs of others. This is an excellent source for men's, women's, and single's ministries.

Relational First Aid

Through *Relational First Aid*, participants will learn how to identify relationship needs such as attention, affection, and respect. You'll learn practical tools for all care-giving relationships and how to see the needs beneath a person's deeds. This is an excellent resource for anyone who hopes to increase their skills for healthy relationships.

LEADERSHIP

Relational Leadership

This resource focuses on the rediscovery of New Testament principles for leadership in the body of Christ. These principles center on the leadership style of Jesus, who led through caring, connected relationships, rather than positional power and formal influence.

DISCIPLESHIP

Relational Discipleship

This resource is designed to help participants discover God's purpose and calling for their lives and to encourage believers to pursue the lifelong, life-changing process of becoming like Jesus. This process, which is often referred to as discipleship or spiritual formation, is fundamentally relational in nature. The *Relational Discipleship* resource is a recommended continuation study.

Transforming Love

The secret to life change doesn't lay in our ability to do the right things or know the right answers. The key to life change is our consistent experience of God's love. This resource will include specific times to encounter Jesus, experience Scripture, and enjoy fellowship with God's people. You'll learn the secrets to spiritual transformation and rediscover a faith that thrives!

SPIRITUAL GROWTH

Praying with Jesus

Jesus is praying, but are we praying with Him? We may pray because Jesus told us to pray or because He modeled prayer, but there is so much more to this mysterious conversation, this divine opportunity. This unique resource is designed to help RESET your prayer life. If you listen closely, you'll hear what He is praying—for the burdens of your heart and the needs of your life. The Savior is praying for you.

Cry Out to the Lord

This collection from twenty different authors seeks to encourage followers of Jesus in living a lifestyle of loving God and others, loving His Word and His mission to see others follow Him through 20 unique studies in how to develop a Spirit-empowered faith.

Honor Your Father

When lived out, the command to "honor your father and your mother" can change the trajectory of generations. Through 80 exercises, outlined in this book, you will be better equipped to honor your heavenly Father, pray for your family's legacy, develop a tribute to your father, and pass on a generational blessing to your children.

31 Days of Prayer For My Husband

Jesus is praying for your husband, and He is inviting you to join Him in those prayers. This resource provides: true stories from wives praying for their husbands to help you understand common challenges and opportunities for men, Scriptures, prayers, and promises to declare over yourself and your husband. It is a practical resource for personal devotions, couples' study, small groups, and men's or women's ministries.

31 Days of Prayer For My Wife

Jesus is praying for your wife, and He is inviting you to join Him in those prayers. This resource provides: true stories from husbands praying for their wives to help you understand common challenges and opportunities for women, Scriptures, prayers, and promises to declare over yourself and your wife. This is a practical resource for personal devotions, couples' study, small groups, and men's or women's ministries.

31 Days of Prayer For My Children

This resource, in the 31 Days of Prayer series, calls our attention to connect with God's heart for our children. Jesus is praying for our children, and He's inviting us to join Him in those prayers. Hear from other parents and their heart for their children to grow in love for God and other people.

31 Days of Prayer For My Pastor

Church members need care, counsel, wisdom, and direction. People outside the church need the gospel. These demands create unique pressures for every pastor. This resource helps churches establish a prayer team to support and encourage their pastor through prayer.

31 Days of Prayer For My Nation

With devotional contributions from National Day of Prayers leaders, staff and friends —including Ronnie Floyd, Dave Butts, Kim Butts, Jon Graf, Tony Evans, Kay Horner, Sammy Rodriguez, Alton Garrison, Tom Phillips, Francis Chan, Tony Perkins, and Oscar Thompson—*31 Days of Prayer For My Nation* provides: guided prayer points for our nation's unity and leaders, prayers for spiritual awakening in the church and global gospel witness, Scriptures, prayers, and promises to declare over your nation.

Made in the USA
Middletown, DE
17 February 2021